D0550124

PHYSICS OF MATERIALS

Other titles in the Project

Physics   Robert Hutchings
Telecommunications   John Allen
Medical Physics   Martin Hollins
Energy and Transport   Robert Hutchings and David Sang
Nuclear and Particle Physics   David Sang

Biology   Martin Rowland
Applied Genetics   Geoff Hayward
Applied Ecology   Geoff Hayward
Micro-organisms and Biotechnology   Jane Taylor
Biochemistry and Molecular Biology   Moira Sheehan

Chemistry   Steve Gurr and Ken Gadd

UNIVERSITY OF BATH • SCIENCE 16-19

Project Director: J. J. Thompson, CBE

PHYSICS OF
MATERIALS

BRIAN COOKE

DAVID SANG

Nelson

Thomas Nelson and Sons Ltd
Nelson House   Mayfield Road
Walton-on-Thames   Surrey
KT12 5PL   UK

Thomas Nelson Australia
102 Dodds Street
South Melbourne
Victoria 3205   Australia

Nelson Canada
1120 Birchmount Road
Scarborough   Ontario
M1K 5G4   Canada

 Thomas Nelson is an International Thomson Publishing Company.

 is used under licence.

ISBN 0-17-448240-X
NPN 9 8 7 6 5 4 3 2 1

Printed in Spain

Contents

The **University of Bath • Science 16–19 Project** grew out of reappraisal of how far sixth form science had travelled during a period of unprecedented curriculum reform and an attempt to evaluate future development. Changes were occurring both within the constitution of 16–19 syllabuses themselves and as a result of external pressures from 16+ and below: syllabus redefinition (starting with the common cores); the introduction of AS-level and its academic recognition; the originally optimistic outcome to the Higginson enquiry; new emphasis on skills and processes; and the balance of continuous and final assessment at GCSE level.

This activity offered fertile ground for the School of Education at the University of Bath to join forces with a team of science teachers, drawn from a wide spectrum of educational experience, to create a flexible curriculum model and then develop resources to fit it. The group addressed the task of satisfying these requirements:

- the new syllabus and examination demands of A- and AS-level courses;
- the provision of materials suitable for both the core and options parts of syllabuses;
- the striking of an appropriate balance of opportunities for students to acquire knowledge and understanding, to develop skills and concepts, and to appreciate the applications and implications of science;
- the encouragement of a degree of independent learning through highly interactive texts;
- the satisfaction of the needs of a wide ability range of students at this level.

Some of these objectives were easier to achieve than others. Relationships to still evolving syllabuses demand the most rigorous analysis and a sense of vision – and optimism – regarding their eventual destination. Original assumptions about AS-level, for example, as a distinct though complementary sibling to A-level, needed to be revised.

The Project, though, always regarded itself as more than a provider of materials, important as this is, and concerned itself equally with the process of provision – how material can best be written and shaped to meet the requirements of the educational market-place. This aim found expression in two principal forms: the idea of secondment at the University and the extensive trialling of early material in schools and colleges.

Most authors enjoyed a period of secondment from teaching, which allowed them not only to reflect and write more strategically (and, particularly so, in a supportive academic environment) but, equally, to engage with each other in wrestling with the issues in question.

The Project saw in the trialling a crucial test for the acceptance of its ideas and their execution. Over one hundred institutions and one thousand students participated, and responses were invited from teachers and pupils alike. The reactions generally confirmed the soundness of the model and allowed for more scrupulous textual housekeeping, as details of confusion, ambiguity or plain misunderstanding were revised and reordered.

The test of all teaching must be in the quality of the learning, and the proof of these resources will be in the understanding and ease of accessibility that they generate. The Project, ultimately, is both a collection of materials and a message of faith in the science curriculum of the future.

J.J. Thompson

How to use this book

Materials science is a branch of science that draws on many disciplines – materials scientists are expected to know about physics and chemistry, and they may also find themselves working alongside engineers, earth scientists, economists and managers. This book focuses on the physics of materials, although it does occasionally stray into areas that might traditionally be thought of as chemistry.

Materials science has developed over the centuries from an empirical subject to one in which an understanding of the underlying structure and behaviour of matter has allowed us to design materials to meet very exacting requirements. No longer is steel, for example, produced according to a recipe derived from trial-and-error experience; nowadays, metallurgists have designed thousands of different steels with compositions that match the demands of a great variety of users.

There are aspects of the physics of materials in all A- and AS-level physics courses, and in Advanced GNVQ Science. This book covers these requirements, and is particularly intended to help students who are following optional topics that look in more depth at mechanical and electronic properties.

The book is divided into three themes. The first covers what we know about the structure of materials, from the microscopic scale of atoms and electrons to the macroscopic scale of crystals and grains. The second theme considers mechanical properties of materials, and uses the ideas from the first theme to show how we can explain how materials respond to mechanical forces in terms of their structure. The third theme deals with electrical, magnetic and optical properties in the same way.

A general theme of the book is the way in which materials scientists can design and improve materials to make them meet ever more demanding requirements. We make use of thousands of different materials in our lives, and many of the devices that we use could not exist were it not for the work of materials scientists. It is only because of our scientific understanding of the structure and properties of materials that technologists and engineers are able to produce these devices.

We have included questions throughout the text to help you to test your understanding of the subject. In addition, we have included assignments and investigations, which encourage you to apply your understanding outside the confines of this book. Examination questions are also included to show you the standard expected at the end of each theme.

We have assumed that you have someone to guide your learning, and to help out if you get really stuck. We have tried to write this book so that it will support your learning; but if in doubt, ask your teacher.

The physics of materials is not the easiest of subjects; there are some quite demanding ideas, and you will need to extend your understanding of the underlying structure of matter. However, because it draws on many of the ideas that you have studied at GCSE and earlier in your A-level course, we hope that you will find that this study will help you to develop a clearer overview of physics as you make use of some of the most fundamental ideas of the subject.

Materials science is an ever-developing subject, and we have included some examples of modern applications of materials. In Appendix B you will find a discussion of the work of materials scientists, and of the career opportunities in this field.

Learning objectives

These are given at the beginning of each chapter, and they outline what you should gain from the chapter. They are statements of attainment and often link closely to statements in a course syllabus. Learning objectives can help you to make notes for revision, especially if used in conjunction with the summaries at the ends of the chapters, as well as for checking progress.

Questions

In-text questions occur at points when you should consolidate what you have just learned, or prepare for what is to follow by thinking along the lines required by the question. Some questions can, therefore, be answered from the material covered in the previous section, while others may require additional thought or information. Answers to numerical questions are given at the end of the book.

Examination questions

At the end of each theme is a group of examination questions relating to the topics covered in that theme. These can be used to help consolidate understanding of the theme or for revision at the end of the course.

Investigations

There are a variety of experiments that you can carry out to investigate the properties and structures of materials. We have included details of several at appropriate points in the text. Where the topic may be relatively unfamiliar, we have included more detailed instructions.

Assignments

Where you are asked to think about a particular idea, or to develop an idea further, you will find text and questions presented together as an assignment. Sometimes these will require you to refer to other resources, some of which are suggested in Appendix D.

Summaries

Each chapter ends with a brief summary of its content. These summaries, together with the learning objectives, should give you a clear overview of the subject, and allow you to check your own progress.

Case studies

We have included a number of case studies at appropriate points in the text. These draw on the topic that you have just been studying, and are intended to show you how an understanding of materials science can be applied to solving a variety of problems.

Other resources

At some points, we have assumed that you will have access to other books, leaflets and videos. Some possible sources are suggested in Appendix D. Materials science is a constantly developing subject, with new materials and new applications coming along all the time. You should look out for articles in this field in periodicals such as *New Scientist* and *Scientific American*, as well as in the science pages of newspapers and magazines.

Acknowledgements

This book is a revised and extended version of *Physics of Materials* by Brian Cooke and David Sang, published by The University of Leeds. The authors are grateful to Fred Archenhold and Colin Wood-Robinson of the Centre for Studies in Science and Mathematics Education, University of Leeds, for arranging for permission to use material from the original book in the present version.

The authors and publishers wish to acknowledge, with thanks, the following photographic sources:

A. F. Kersting: *Fig 4.18, page 43;* AEA Technology Culham/Harwell Photographic Group: *Fig 2.1, page 13; Fig 4.14, page 41;* Alfred Pasieka/Science Photo Library: *Fig 3.3, page 28;* Andrew Lambert: *Fig 7.7, page 86; Fig 8.9, page 102; Fig 8.11, page 103;* BT Pictures: *Fig 6.14, page 80;* Chemical Design Limited/Science Photo Library: *Fig 7.31, page 95;* Chris Bland/Eye Ubiquitous: *Fig 4.27, page 48;* D. Holland/Department of Physics, University of Warwick: *Fig 3.9, page 31;* David Guyon/Science Photo Library: *Fig 1.2, page 3;* Department of Materials, Oxford University: *Fig 5.5(c), page 52;* Department of Physics, Imperial College/Science Photo Library: *Fig 6.2, page 73;* IBM: *Figure 1.1, page 2;* J. Allan Cash: *Fig 4.5 and 4.6, page 38; Fig 6.8, page 77;* John Greim/Science Photo Library: *Fig 7.25, page 93;* Lead Sheet Association: *Fig 5.14, page 58;* Malcolm Fielding, The BOC Group PLC/Science Photo Library: *Fig 3.2, page 28;* NASA: *Theme 1 intro figs (a), (b) and (c);* Philippe Plailly/Science Photo Library: *Fig 8.14, page 105;* Rolls-Royce plc: *Figs 5.26(b) and 5.27, page 65; Figs 5.28(b) and 5.30(b), page 66; Fig 5.31, page 67;* Royal Mint: *Fig 5.4, page 52;* Science Photo Library: *Fig 7.29, page 94;* Sir John Charnley/MacQuitty Collection: *Theme 2 Intro fig, page 35;* The University of Leeds: *Fig 2.9, page 16; Fig 2.10, page 17; Fig 2.11, page 17; Fig 2.12(a), (b) and (c), page 17; Fig 2.13(a), (b), (c) and (d), page 18; Fig 2.14(a) and (b), page 18; Fig 2.15, page 19; Fig 2.17(a) and (b), page 20; Fig 2.18, page 21; Fig 2.22, page 22; Figs 2.24, 2.25, 2.26, 2.27 and 2.28; Fig 2.30, page 24; Fig 2.31, page 25; Fig 3.6(a) and (b), page 30; Fig 3.8, page 30; Fig 3.12(a) and (b), page 32; Fig 4.1, page 36* ('Coca-Cola', 'Coke', the Dynamic Ribbon device and the design of the contour bottle are registered trade marks of The Coca-Cola Company); *Fig 4.9, page 39; Fig 5.7, page 53; Fig 5.15(b) and (c), page 58; Fig 5.16(a) and (b), page 59; Theme 3 intro fig, page 71; Fig 9.1, page 107; Fig 9.7, page 111;* Unilab: *Fig 7.21, page 91;* University of St Andrews: *Fig 7.28, page 94;* Vidali Synagogue: *Fig 7.22, page 92.*

Every effort has been made to trace all the copyright holders, but if any have been inadvertently overlooked the publishers will be pleased to make the necessary arrangement at the first opportunity.

Theme 1

STRUCTURE AND MICROSTRUCTURE

Materials science is an advanced subject. In previous centuries, materials were improved by trial and error, with no understanding of why one material was better than another. In the 20th century, scientists have greatly developed our understanding of the nature of materials. In particular, they have been able to show how the properties of a material are related to its structure. By knowing about the underlying structure of materials, right down to the atomic level, it is possible to design new, improved materials with properties that make it possible to perform many new tasks. In the 21st century, new techniques and new theories will make for new revolutions in materials technology.

Theme 1 deals with the structure of materials. First, we will look at the forces between particles, and the way that particles bond together. Then we will look at the great range of structures that result, from the very ordered to the very disordered, and the different processes used by engineers to alter and control the final structure of materials.

In examining the structure of materials, engineers use many techniques, including X-ray crystallography and optical and electron microscopy. These reveal the small-scale structure of solids, which is often invisible to the naked eye – the microstructure of the material.

(b) Under normal gravity, latex particles show the influence of gravity in their deformed shapes, inconsistent sizes and other imperfections.

(c) In space, the particles are much more regular in shape and arrangement.

(a) The Space Shuttle Columbia, launched in July 1994, carried an experiment to study the effects of weightlessness on materials production. Photographs (b) and (c) show the advantages of processing latex in space.

Chapter 1

FORCES AND BONDING

We are surrounded by materials, some natural, many synthetic. It is hard to imagine the sort of life we would lead without the material artefacts on which we rely today. In this chapter, we will look at the particles of which all materials are made, and the forces that hold them together.

LEARNING OBJECTIVES

After studying this chapter you should be able to:

1. describe the interaction between two neutral atoms in terms of attractive and repulsive forces and associated potential energy;

2. use the relationship between force, distance and potential energy to interpret force–distance and potential energy–distance graphs;

3. use correctly the terms 'equilibrium separation' and 'binding energy', and relate these terms to the force–distance and potential energy–distance graphs;

4. relate Hooke's law and thermal expansion to the force–distance and energy–distance graphs;

5. describe the three primary bonds (covalent, ionic and metallic) and the secondary van der Waals bond – their origins and directionality.

1.1 MATERIALS AROUND US

Introduction

Take a look at some of the materials around you now: paper, plastic, wood, metal, glass. You see a vast array of materials, each one with its own uses. Nowadays, we even have synthetic materials inside us. You may have fillings in your teeth, artificial lenses in your eyes, metal and plastic hip joints, synthetic heart valves and a pacemaker. All these are made from materials designed to survive and function within the human body.

There are synthetic materials orbiting the Earth, on the Moon, flying out past the farthest planets. Plastic bottles are washed up on the shores of desert islands. Synthetic materials are everywhere.

It is our use of materials that is one feature which distinguishes us from our ancestors. Indeed, our use of materials allows us to classify our historical development – think of the Stone Age, Bronze Age, Iron Age, named after the enduring materials left behind by the people of those times. Nowadays, we use too vast a range of materials to name our age after any one dominant material – though perhaps our use of silicon has had a more dramatic effect on our lives than any other material this century (Fig 1.1).

Classifying materials

You should be familiar with the traditional division of materials into four classes: metals, ceramics, polymers and composites. These may be described briefly as follows.

Fig 1.1 Silicon chips (integrated circuits) are prepared in very clean production facilities, like this one at IBM.

Metals

Copper, aluminium and steel are familiar examples. Metals may consist of atoms of a single chemical element, or they may have other elements blended into them. Typically, metals are strong, are good conductors of heat and electricity, and may be formed into useful shapes by casting, forging, pressing, etc.

Ceramics

Porcelain, brick and glass are examples. Ceramics are chemical compounds, often oxides or nitrides. They are chemically inert and have high melting points. They are generally brittle, which makes them difficult to form. Typically, ceramics are made by mixing the starting material with water, shaping it, and then firing it in an oven to give the final product. (This is the familiar way in which pottery is made from clay.)

Polymers

Polythene, perspex and rubber are examples. Polymers are organic compounds, consisting of very large molecules formed by joining together many smaller ones (monomers). They may be subdivided into 'thermoplastics', which may be readily moulded into a desired shape when warm, and 'thermosets', which are hard, brittle and difficult to shape after polymerisation. Polythene and nylon are thermoplastics; melamine and bakelite are thermosets.

Composites

Glass-fibre-reinforced plastic and reinforced concrete are examples of synthetic composite materials. They are made of two or more components. The aim is to combine the desirable properties of the different components, to give a better final material than the individual components alone. Many natural materials are composites. Wood consists of cellulose fibres in a lignin matrix; bone is collagen fibres in a calcium compound matrix. Both materials are very strong when compressed, and can support large loads.

This classification has its origins in the historical development of materials technology. Metals were the concern of the iron and steel trade, ceramics were the province of the pottery industry, and polymers derived from the chemical and petroleum industries.

Nowadays we can take a more general view across the whole spectrum of materials. We can make metals that are glassy, ceramics that conduct electricity, polymers as stiff as steel, and crystals that are liquid. All these are the achievements of materials scientists and engineers.

Materials engineering

A materials engineer, working in industry, must collaborate closely with many other specialists concerned with the manufacturing process (Fig 1.2). They may be mechanical engineers, electrical engineers, production engineers, designers, marketing staff. It is the role of the materials engineer to know about materials and their properties, their costs, availability, fabrication and so on, and to share this information with others so that sensible manufacturing decisions are taken.

To become a skilled materials engineer takes education, and practical experience in the handling of materials. You already know quite a lot about many familiar materials in common use, information you have picked up in everyday life and at school or college.

Fig 1.2 A materials engineer must work closely with other specialists as part of a team in industry.

Try the following questions, to see how much you already know about materials. The answers illustrate the wide range of aspects of materials with which a materials engineer must be familiar.

1.1 Which is the better electrical conductor, copper or silver?

1.2 Why is copper generally used in preference to silver for wiring?

1.3 Why are plastic saucepan handles preferable to metal ones?

1.4 Why was lead used for water pipes for many centuries?

1.5 What advantage does fibreglass have over steel for a ship's hull?

A better classification

Why do different materials have different properties? You will probably say that this is because they are composed of different chemical elements in different combinations. This is quite true, but there is more to it than this.

The electrical resistivity of diamond is 10^{17} times that of graphite, and yet they are both forms of the element carbon. The difference lies in the internal arrangement of the atoms – the way in which the atoms are bonded together.

In Theme 1 we will look at the way in which materials may be described in terms of the arrangement of the particles of which they are composed – in other words, the structure of the materials. Some materials are highly ordered, that is, the particles are arranged in a regular array. Other materials are relatively disordered. We can classify materials on a scale from highly ordered (crystalline) to highly disordered (amorphous).

Material properties

Different materials have had greater or lesser importance at different times in our history, and in different parts of the world. New materials are constantly being designed and brought into use. However, we can study materials properties – mechanical, electrical, magnetic, optical, thermal, chemical, etc. – and then apply our knowledge to new materials as they come along.

In Themes 2 and 3, you can concentrate on studying some of the more important physical properties of materials. While it is not essential to learn in detail about particular materials, you will pick up some information about some of the more common materials in use today. You will also see how the properties of materials can be controlled by controlling the structure of the material, to give a product that will satisfy a purpose.

A materials engineer may become expert in the vast range of complex multi-component alloys used in aero engineering. These change year by year. However, the principles remain the same, as we seek greater control over the properties of the material by controlling its structure.

1.2 FORCES BETWEEN PARTICLES

In this theme, we are looking at the structure of solids – how they are made up from their constituent particles. These particles may be atoms, ions or molecules. We will use the general term 'particle' to cover all of these.

REVISION ASSIGNMENT

If you are not sure of the meanings of the terms 'atom', 'ion' and 'molecule', check up on them now. Write an illustrated note to explain the differences between these three types of particle.

When a gas is cooled, the particles coalesce to form first a liquid and then a solid. The simplest kinetic theory model of a gas assumes that the particles do not attract each other; they simply bounce apart when they collide. When a solid forms, it must be as a result of attractive forces between the particles. There are also repulsive forces between them.

What evidence do we have of the existence of attractive and repulsive forces between the atoms or molecules that make up matter? Think about the three states of matter, and what happens when you try to stretch or squeeze a solid object.

A cool gas condenses because the particles are moving more slowly, and the attractive forces make them stick together to form a liquid or solid. When you stretch a piece of wire, you are pulling against the attractive forces between the atoms of the metal. When you sit on a chair, the repulsive forces between the molecules stop it being crushed beneath you.

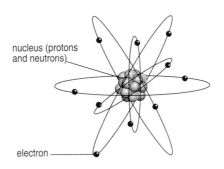

nucleus (protons and neutrons)

electron

Fig 1.3 In a neutral atom, the number of orbiting electrons equals the number of protons in the nucleus.

Origin of the forces

Every atom (Fig 1.3) is composed of equal numbers of oppositely charged particles – protons and electrons – and so is electrically neutral. However, the protons of one atom may attract the electrons of another atom, or they may repel the protons of another. The electrons of one atom will also repel the electrons of another. These simple **electrostatic forces** between charges are the origin of the attractive and repulsive forces that act in a solid. The force between two neutral atoms is rather weak, and is known as the **van der Waals force**.

The magnitude of the force F that one particle exerts on another depends on their distance apart r, according to an inverse power law:

$$F \propto 1/r^n$$

You may be familiar with Coulomb's law, which says that for two charged particles

$$F \propto 1/r^2$$

that is $n = 2$.

For net uncharged (neutral) particles, n is a number usually greater than 6, which depends on whether the force is attractive or repulsive.

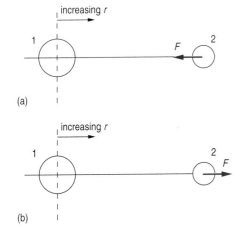

(a)

(b)

Fig 1.4

Sign convention

Before looking in more detail at these forces, we need to adopt a sign convention for the direction of the force. Look at Fig 1.4. In both cases, particle 1 is exerting a force F on particle 2, along the r axis. A force in the direction of increasing r is considered to be positive.

Which force is positive and which is negative? Which is attractive and which is repulsive?

We can summarise this: repulsive forces are positive, attractive forces are negative. In sketching the form of the force between two particles, we use axes such that the positive direction represents repulsion – see Fig 1.5.

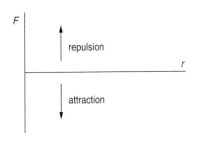

Fig 1.5 Repulsive forces are positive, attractive forces are negative.

Graphical representation

Fig 1.6 is a graph that shows how the repulsive force, and the attractive force, between two particles depend on their separation r.

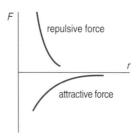

Fig 1.6 Graphs to show how the attractive and repulsive forces between two particles depend on their separation.

QUESTION

1.6 Study the curves in Fig 1.6, which represent the attractive and repulsive forces between two particles.

(a) Which is greater for small r? For large r?

(b) Does this suggest that particles will tend to attract or repel one another when they are far apart? Will they attract or repel when they are close together?

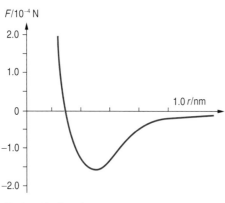

Fig 1.7 The force between two neutral krypton atoms.

The resultant force between the two particles is the sum of the attractive and repulsive components. Fig 1.7 shows how the resultant force between two krypton atoms depends on their separation. Note the point where the curve crosses the r axis. The resultant force here is zero; this is called the **equilibrium separation** r_0.

Think about two particles, initially separated by a distance r_0. If they are pulled apart to a slightly greater separation and released, what will happen? If they are pushed together and released, what will happen?

For separations greater than r_0, the attractive force dominates and returns the particles towards equilibrium. For separations less than r_0, the repulsive force returns the particles towards equilibrium.

QUESTIONS

1.7 Study the graph in Fig 1.7, which shows the force between two neutral krypton atoms.

(a) At what separation is the force between them zero? In other words, what is their equilibrium separation r_0?

(b) At what separation is the attractive force between them greatest? Which point on the graph represents this?

1.8 Two frictionless trolleys have their spring-loads released, and carry strongly attracting magnets as shown in Fig 1.8.

(a) Explain what will happen if they are brought together.

(b) Sketch the force–separation curve between the two vehicles.

(c) Explain the shape of the graph in terms of the two forces acting.

(d) Explain why this graph is similar in shape to the force–separation graph for two neutral atoms.

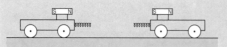

Fig 1.8 Two trolleys with magnets – a model system with attractive and repulsive forces.

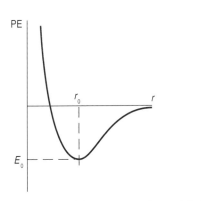

Fig 1.9 Potential energy–separation graph for two neutral atoms.

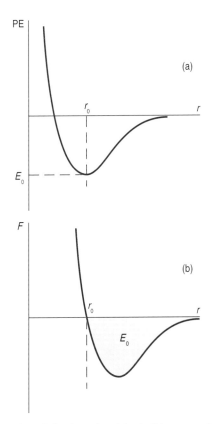

Fig 1.10 Graphs to show **(a)** potential energy and **(b)** force, for two neutral atoms as a function of their separation.

Potential energy

Changing the separation of the particles requires work to be done; their potential energy changes.

Imagine two particles that are initially separated by the equilibrium separation r_0. If you push them together, you have to do work. You increase their potential energy. Similarly, if you pull them apart from r_0, you have to do work on them, and their potential energy increases. It follows that their potential energy must have its minimum value at r_0.

If you pull them apart strongly enough, they will completely separate. We define their potential energy to be zero when they are a long way apart. Since work must be done on the particles to pull them apart, it follows that their potential energy is less than zero at r_0.

Fig 1.9 shows how the potential energy of two neutral atoms depends on their separation. It is easiest to understand this graph if you start at the right-hand end. Here, the atoms are an infinite distance apart and their potential energy (PE) is zero. As they come closer together, their PE decreases, until it is a minimum at r_0. They must be pushed to get them closer together than r_0, and so their PE increases beyond this point.

If two atoms are at their equilibrium separation, work must be done to pull them apart. The amount of energy required is known as the **binding energy**, and this is shown on the graph as E_0.

Force and energy

The two graphs, for force (Fig 1.7) and for energy (Fig 1.9), have very similar shapes and are easily confused. We will now look at the connection between (i) force, (ii) distance moved in the direction of the force and (iii) energy, to see how the two graphs are linked. To make the relationship clearer, the two graphs are shown, one above the other, in Fig 1.10.

You should be familiar with the equation:

$$\text{work done} = \text{force} \times (\text{distance moved in direction of force})$$

To find the change in potential energy, we need to find the work done in bringing the particles together. Looking at the force graph, this is given by the area under the graph (because the area under the graph is force × distance). The area shown shaded in Fig 1.10(b) is the energy of the particles at r_0, i.e. their binding energy.

Looking at the energy graph in Fig 1.10(a), we can find the force at any separation by finding the gradient of the curve. This follows if we rearrange the equation for work done:

$$\text{force} = (\text{work done})/(\text{distance moved in direction of force})$$

At r_0, the gradient of the energy graph is zero, so the force is zero. At greater separations, the gradient is positive and the force is negative.

ASSIGNMENT

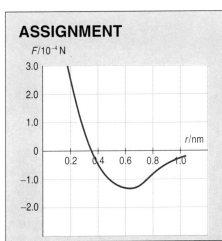

Fig 1.11 Force–separation graph.

Fig 1.11 shows the force–separation graph for two atoms.

1.9 Use the graph to deduce the following quantities:

    (a) their equilibrium separation r_0;

    (b) their binding energy E_0.

1.10 Sketch an energy–separation graph for the two atoms. Mark on it the values of r_0 and E_0.

(The force is in the opposite direction to r – remember the sign convention.) So the two graphs are related as follows:

potential energy = area under force–separation graph

force = – (gradient of energy–separation graph)

(Strictly speaking, we should have used calculus to deduce these relationships.)

Using the graphs

When a solid object is stretched or squeezed, the separation of the particles varies about r_0. When a solid is heated, the particles vibrate about r_0 with greater amplitude and the solid expands. We can use the force–distance and energy–distance graphs to explain the origins of Hooke's law and thermal expansion.

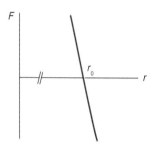

Fig 1.12 Force–separation graph around r_0.

Hooke's law says that, when an object is subjected to a tensile (stretching) or compressive (squashing) force, the change in its length is proportional to the applied force. A force–extension graph is a straight line. This linear behaviour arises from the shape of the force–separation graph for two atoms. Fig 1.12 shows a magnified view of the region around r_0. The graph is a straight line (to a good approximation) in this region. As an object is stretched, the atoms of which it consists are pulled apart very slightly. Because the graph is straight, it follows that the increase in length is proportional to the force. (For larger forces, the graph is curved, and Hooke's law is no longer obeyed. Eventually, the maximum possible force is reached, the atoms pull apart, and the material breaks.)

What happens when a material is compressed? Because the graph is a straight line, we can deduce that the material will also obey Hooke's law when it is subject to a compressive force. The gradient of the force–compression graph will be the same as for the force–extension graph. In other words, it is as easy to compress a material as it is to stretch it.

Thermal expansion can be understood by looking at the energy–separation graph for two neighbouring atoms. When the atoms are very cold, they sit at their equilibrium separation r_0. If the material is warmed, the atoms gain energy and start to vibrate. This is shown in Fig 1.13. The atoms oscillate inside the 'energy well', like two atoms joined by a spring. As their energy increases at higher temperatures, they oscillate with greater amplitude.

The dashed line in Fig 1.13 shows the midpoint of these oscillations. At higher energies, the midpoint of the oscillations is at an increased separation. In other words, at higher temperatures, the average separation of the atoms is greater. Each atom occupies more space, and the material expands. (Note that it is the fact that the energy well is not symmetrical that ultimately gives rise to this expansion. If the well was symmetrical, the dashed line in Fig 1.13 would not bend to the right.)

Hence we have seen how two macroscopic (large-scale) phenomena – Hooke's law and thermal expansion – can be explained in terms of the microscopic (small-scale) nature of the forces between atoms.

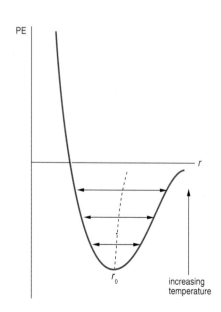

Fig 1.13 The equilibrium separation of two atoms increases as the temperature rises.

FORCES AND BONDING

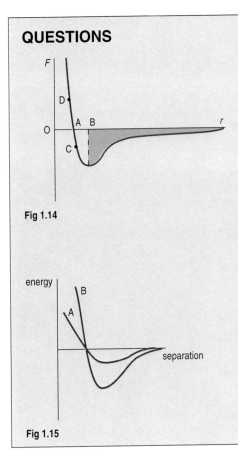

Fig 1.14

Fig 1.15

1.11 The diagram in Fig 1.14 shows the way in which the force *F* between two neutral particles depends on their separation *r*. Which of the following statements is/are correct? In each case, explain your answer.

(a) The part of the curve below the *r* axis represents an attractive force.

(b) The distance OB represents the equilibrium separation of the particles.

(c) Hooke's law is a consequence of the linearity of the graph over the region AC.

(d) The shaded area represents the binding energy of the two particles.

(e) If the region of the graph AD was steeper, a material made of these particles would be less compressible.

1.12 The melting point of a solid is another property that depends on the energy–separation graph. Fig 1.15 shows the energy–separation graphs for two solids, A and B.

(a) Which solid will have the higher melting point? Explain your answer.

(b) Which solid will expand more on heating? Explain your answer.

1.3 BONDING

Table 1.1 Outer electrons in neutral atoms of Groups I, II, VI and VII

Group	Examples	Number of outer electrons
I	Li, Na, K	1
II	Mg, Ca	2
VI	O, S	6
VII	F, Br, Cl	7

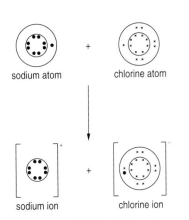

Fig 1.16 Representing ionic bonding in sodium chloride.

Primary bonds

When two oxygen atoms combine, they form a molecule of gaseous oxygen O_2. The atoms are held together by a strong electrostatic force known as a **primary bond**. Large numbers of particles can also be held together by primary bonds to form giant three-dimensional structures such as sodium chloride, diamond or copper. (These structures are discussed in Chapter 2.) There are three types of primary bond: ionic, covalent and metallic.

Ionic bonds

Typical ionic bonds are formed between atoms of metallic elements in Group I or Group II of the Periodic Table and non-metallic elements of Group VI or VII – see Table 1.1. When reactions between these elements occur, electrons are transferred from the metal atom to the non-metal atom. The metal atom becomes a positive ion (because it has lost negatively charged electrons), and the non-metal atom becomes a negative ion. The resulting electrostatic attraction between the ions forms the ionic bond. The force is relatively strong, and ionic solids generally have to be heated to a high temperature before they will melt.

As a result of the electron transfer, each ion acquires a full outer shell of eight electrons. A metal atom loses all of the electrons from its outer shell, so that its penultimate full shell becomes the outer shell of the ion. A non-metal atom gains electrons to fill its outer shell.

Fig 1.16 shows how sodium chloride is formed by the transfer of a single electron from sodium to chlorine. In this diagram, the electrons of the sodium atom are represented as dots, while the electrons of chlorine are shown as crosses. (In reality, all electrons are identical, and they are distributed within the atoms as diffuse clouds of charge.)

For simplicity, only the two outermost shells of electrons are shown. You will notice that both ions have full outer shells of eight electrons.

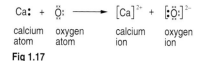

calcium atom   oxygen atom   calcium ion   oxygen ion

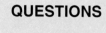

These dot-and-cross diagrams can be simplified further by considering only the outermost electrons. Fig 1.17 shows the electron transfers that occur when calcium oxide forms.

QUESTIONS

1.13 How many electrons are transferred in the formation of CaO (Fig 1.17)?

1.14 Draw dot-and-cross diagrams to show the formation of ionic bonds in the following substances (Table 1.1 will help):

    (a) potassium fluoride KF,

    (b) magnesium sulphide MgS,

    (c) lithium oxide Li_2O.

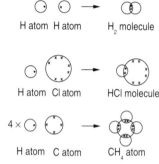

H atom   H atom H_2 molecule

H atom   Cl atom   HCl molecule

$4 \times$ H atom   C atom CH_4 atom

Fig 1.18 Covalent bonding.

Covalent bonds

Elements in the middle of the Periodic Table do not form ionic compounds. Their atoms would have to gain or lose three or four electrons to form ions; these elements form covalent bonds by sharing electrons between atoms. (This type of bond can also form between pairs of atoms both of which need electrons to complete their outer shells, e.g. in the diatomic molecules H_2, O_2 and Cl_2.)

Fig 1.18 shows dot-and-cross diagrams for the formation of covalent bonds in hydrogen H_2, hydrogen chloride HCl, and methane CH_4.

QUESTIONS

1.15 How many covalent bonds are formed in each example shown in Fig 1.18?

1.16 Draw dot-and-cross diagrams to show the formation of covalent bonds in the following:

    (a) oxygen O_2,

    (b) carbon dioxide CO_2,

    (c) water H_2O.

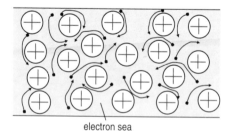

electron sea

Fig 1.19 Metallic bonding.

Metallic bonds

In a metal, some electrons are free to move about within the material. The atoms that have lost (negatively charged) electrons are thus positive ions. They are held together by the presence of the 'sea' of free electrons – see Fig 1.19.

The three types of primary bonds represent ideal forms of bond. In practice, bonds are found to be a mixture of these types.

Secondary bonds

Primary bonds involve the movement or sharing of electrons *between* particles. There are also weaker bonds, which arise from the redistribution of electrons *within* a particle.

Molecules of water, oil and polythene are held together by covalent bonds. However, since these substances can exist as solids and liquids, it follows that there must be attractive forces *between* the molecules, which hold them together. These forces are again electrostatic in origin, but they

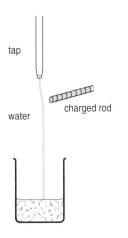

Fig 1.20 An electrostatically charged rod attracts water.

are much weaker than the primary bonds discussed above. They are called **secondary bonds** or **van der Waals bonds**.

You may have seen an experiment in which a stream of water from a tap is attracted towards an electrically charged rod – Fig 1.20. This experiment gives a clue to the origin of these secondary bonds. If we compare similar but slightly different compounds, we find that there is a pattern in the results – see Table 1.2.

Table 1.2 Some liquid streams are deflected in an electric field, but others are not

Compound deflected		Compound not deflected	
trichloromethane	$CHCl_3$	tetrachloromethane	CCl_4
nitrobenzene	$NO_2C_6H_5$	benzene	C_6H_6
cyclohexanol	$C_6H_{11}OH$	cyclohexane	C_6H_{12}

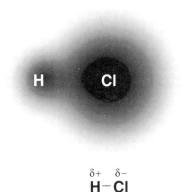

δ+   δ–
H–Cl

Fig 1.21 HCl is a polar molecule.

Those molecules which are not attracted to the charged rod are all symmetrical. A small change in the molecular structure, e.g. from CCl_4 to $CHCl_3$, makes it unsymmetrical. In an unsymmetrical molecule, the distribution of electric charge is distorted. Fig 1.21 shows the distribution of charge in a molecule of hydrogen chloride HCl. The nucleus of the Cl atom attracts the electron cloud more strongly than the nucleus of the H atom, and as a result the centre of negative charge is displaced slightly from the centre of positive charge. The result is known as a **permanent electric dipole**.

Such a dipole is represented by showing a small positive charge δ+ on one part of the molecule, and a small negative charge δ– on another part. The attraction between dipoles on neighbouring molecules gives rise to a weak bond, known as a van der Waals bond. The liquids that are not attracted by the charged rod in the experiment shown in Fig 1.20 have molecules with no permanent dipoles. They are said to be **non-polar**. Only **polar** molecules are deflected by an electric field.

In symmetrical diatomic molecules such as H_2, N_2 or Cl_2, no permanent dipoles can exist. However, there are very weak van der Waals forces between these molecules. They arise because at any instant there may be an unsymmetrical distribution of electrons around the nuclei. The result is an **instantaneous electric dipole** – see Fig 1.22. These dipoles attract one another, and this gives rise to the very weak bonding.

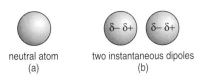

neutral atom
(a)

two instantaneous dipoles
(b)

Fig 1.22 Instantaneous dipoles result in an attraction between two neutral atoms.

QUESTION

1.17 Use the idea of permanent and instantaneous electric dipoles to explain why hydrogen gas condenses (liquefies) at a much lower temperature than hydrogen chloride.

Bond direction

Covalent bonds in a molecule are oriented in specific directions, and the atoms within the molecule have a fixed spatial relationship. As a consequence, discrete molecules such as methane CH_4 and carbon dioxide CO_2 have highly specific shapes – see Fig 1.23. This has clear consequences for the way in which such molecules pack together to form a solid.

Let us now think about the way in which spherical charged ions attract each other. Sodium chloride has ionic bonds formed between positively charged sodium ions and negatively charged chloride ions. An individual sodium ion will attract chloride ions and repel other sodium ions.

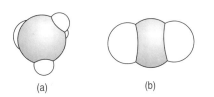

(a)   (b)

Fig 1.23 Models of (a) CH_4, a tetrahedral molecule, and (b) CO_2, a linear molecule.

Table 1.3 Bond energies for some covalent and ionic bonds

Bond type	Bond	Energy/kJ mol⁻¹
Covalent	C—H	413
	C—C	346
	O—O	146
	H—Cl	431
	Si—O	464
	I—I	151
Ionic	NaF	915
	NaCl	780
	$MgCl_2$	2490
	MgO	3933

There is no preferred direction for this attraction. Ionic bonds are not directional – they tend to lead to structures where the particles are packed closely together. Each ion is closely surrounded by a large number of ions of opposite charge.

Similarly the metallic bond is not directional. Metals tend to have close-packed structures.

Bond energy

Primary bonds are much stronger than secondary bonds. Consequently, more energy is needed to break primary bonds than secondary bonds.

Typically, primary bonds break when the temperature is raised to between 1000 K and 5000 K; secondary bonds break between 100 K and 500 K. Hence a primary bond requires roughly ten times as much energy to break it as a secondary bond.

Table 1.3 shows the bond energies of some covalent and ionic bonds. The energy of a van der Waals bond is about one-tenth of that of a covalent bond.

ASSIGNMENT

Copy Table 1.4 into your notes, and complete it.

Table 1.4

Type of bond	Primary/secondary	Directional?	Example of solid
covalent			
ionic			
metallic			
van der Waals			

QUESTION

1.18 Which of the following types of bond:

A covalent   **B** ionic   **C** metallic   **D** van der Waals

(a)   is the sharing of electrons between all identical particles or ions?

(b)   is an attraction between individual molecules?

(c)   is the sharing of electrons between specific atoms?

(d)   is the result of electrostatic forces between ions?

(e)   always has a highly specific direction?

SUMMARY

There are attractive and repulsive forces between the particles (neutral atoms, ions and molecules) of which materials are made. These forces are balanced when the particles are at their equilibrium separation. The energy required to separate them is known as the binding energy.

Hooke's law follows from the fact that the force–separation graph is approximately linear around the equilibrium separation. Thermal expansion can be understood from the energy–separation graph; at higher temperatures, the particles have more energy and their average separation increases.

The forces between particles give rise to bonding between them. There are three types of primary (strong) bonds: ionic, covalent and metallic. Secondary bonds, such as the van der Waals bonding between neutral particles, are weak.

Chapter 2

PACKING PARTICLES

Solids are formed when liquids cool down and when gases condense. The motion of the particles of the substance is reduced, and they usually become closely packed together. We will now look at the different structures that may form, starting with methods that reveal details of the structure of solids.

Fig 2.1 An X-ray diffraction machine, used to identify crystal structures.

LEARNING OBJECTIVES

After studying this chapter you should be able to:

1. use simple models to describe particle packing in solids, including close-packed and more open structures, crystalline, polycrystalline, semicrystalline and amorphous solids;

2. use correctly the following scientific terms: 'coordination number', 'unit cell' and 'anisotropy';

3. use X-ray and electron diffraction patterns to deduce these underlying structures;

4. describe the principal types of point and line defects in solids (vacancies, substitutional, interstitial and edge dislocation), and grains and grain boundaries.

2.1 INVESTIGATING THE STRUCTURE OF SOLIDS

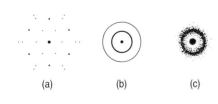

(a)   (b)   (c)

Fig 2.2 Schematic X-ray diffraction patterns for **(a)** single-crystal, **(b)** polycrystalline and **(c)** amorphous materials.

X-ray diffraction

In order to probe the structure of materials at the atomic level, we cannot use visible light – the wavelength is too great. Instead, we use X-rays (short-wavelength electromagnetic radiation) or fast-moving electrons.

In X-ray diffraction, a beam of X-rays shines on to a sample of material. Because the wavelength of the X-rays is comparable with the spacing of the particles of which the material is made, they are diffracted. They spread out to form a **diffraction pattern**, which can give information about the arrangement of the particles. The pattern can show whether the particles are arranged in a regular, ordered way or in an irregular, disordered way. It can also give information about the spacing of the particles.

Fig 2.1 shows an X-ray diffraction machine, used in a research laboratory to investigate the structure of materials. The diffracted X-rays can be detected electronically or by using photographic film. Electronic detectors can be connected via an interface to a computer, which can carry out a detailed analysis of the diffraction pattern.

X-ray crystallography allows us to distinguish between single-crystal, polycrystalline and amorphous (non-crystalline) materials, because they give different patterns – see Fig 2.2. It can also enable us to identify the material that is present. The arrangement and spacings of the rings or spots can be used to determine the crystal structure and spacing of the crystal planes. Knowing these, we may be able to identify the material.

2.1   What are the characteristic differences between the diffraction patterns for the three types of materials shown in Fig 2.2?

INVESTIGATION

An optical analogue of X-ray diffraction

It is unlikely that you will have access to equipment to carry out X-ray diffraction for yourself. This investigation includes some optical analogues (using light), to show you how the diffraction of X-rays and electrons is related to the more familiar ideas of the diffraction of light.

It is best to work in a darkened room. An mes (torch) bulb acts as a point source of light and should be viewed from a distance of about 2 m – see Fig 2.3. Hold the items listed below close to your eye and look at the light source. You should be able to see a diffraction pattern – spots or rings of light around the bulb.

First, try **fabric with a regular structure**, such as a cotton handkerchief or umbrella fabric. Try tilting, stretching and rotating the material and observe the effect on the diffraction pattern. Investigate the effect of changing the spacing of the diffracting centres by using materials that have a closer or coarser weave.

A material like a **nappy liner** can give a diffraction pattern resembling that of a semicrystalline material.

Now look at the lamp through a slide dusted with **lycopodium powder**. How does the pattern differ from that of a rotating handkerchief? How are the particles arranged on the slide? You may need a microscope to see this.

If you have a set of **Nuffield diffraction grids**, look at the diffraction patterns that they produce. Examine the 'particle' arrangement on the grids and decide how the diffraction pattern changes as the separation and arrangement of the 'particles' is changed.

Investigate how the pattern spacing changes with wavelength by using coloured filters to look at one of your diffracting arrays.

What happens to the spread of the pattern as the wavelength

Fig 2.3

Interpreting diffraction patterns

The pattern that you see using the fabric or the diffraction grids resembles the X-ray pattern shown in Fig 2.2(a). The regular array of holes produces an optical diffraction pattern similar to that for X-rays diffracted by planes of atoms in a **single crystal**.

If you rotate the array of holes in a series of steps, each diffraction pattern spot rotates through an arc. Each step corresponds to a reorientation of the single crystal. If a very large number of orientations are present, the single spots become circles. Hence X-ray diffraction patterns of **polycrystalline** materials consist of sets of concentric circles – Fig 2.2(b).

Closer separations result in diffraction patterns with wider spacings. Disordered patterns give fuzzy rings. The lycopodium dust gives two rings. This sort of pattern is observed when X-rays are diffracted by disordered or amorphous solids – Fig 2.2(c).

Atomic spacings

X-rays are diffracted by an array of atoms, but visible light is not. By considering the wavelengths of X-rays and visible light, what can be inferred about the spacing of atoms in solids? As planes of atoms diffract X-rays, which have shorter wavelength than visible light, the atomic planes must be closer together than the 'particles' of the diffraction grids or holes in the fabric samples.

2.2   Visible light and X-rays are both types of electromagnetic radiation. Find out the wavelength ranges for both.

2.3   Use a data book to find out values for the spacings of atoms in some materials, e.g. copper, diamond, sodium chloride.

2.4   Use the information from 2.3 above to explain why X-rays are appropriate for investigating the structure of solid materials.

2.5   An electron beam can be focused down to a very fine point – less than 1 μm across. What advantage does this give electron diffraction over X-rays?

Powders, polycrystalline and amorphous materials

If a single crystal is crushed to form a powder of very small crystals (crystallites), the X-ray or electron diffraction pattern is found to consist of concentric rings. Within each crystallite, the atoms, ions or molecules form a regular array. However, the arrays within different crystallites are oriented differently – see Fig 2.4. The diffraction spots from each crystallite combine to give rings, because there are crystallites oriented in all directions.

Many metals and ceramics are found to give ring diffraction patterns. This tells us that metals and ceramics generally have polycrystalline structures.

Other materials may be non-crystalline. Glass is such an 'amorphous' material. When molten glass is cooled quickly, the molecules do not have time to reach an ordered arrangement. They retain the random orientation they had in the liquid state – see Fig 2.5. Many other materials show this amorphous state. If sugar is melted and then cooled rapidly, it forms a clear glass-like solid – the toffee used for toffee apples. If this becomes crystalline, the solid becomes cloudy – fudge.

If molten metal is sprayed onto a cold surface, its temperature drops rapidly – perhaps as fast as one thousand degrees in a millisecond (see Fig 2.6). A disordered, amorphous material is formed with the electrical and magnetic properties of a metal. Amorphous metals are already proving useful in low-energy-loss transformer cores.

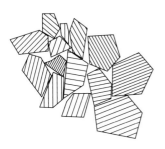

Fig 2.4   In a powder, the arrays of atoms are oriented differently in different grains.

Fig 2.5   In a glassy material, there is no long-range ordering. The diagram is a two-dimensional representation of such a structure.

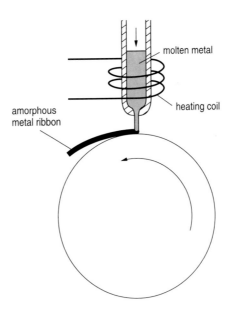

Fig 2.6   An amorphous metal is produced by ultra-rapid cooling. Metal is melted in a quartz tube, and is then sprayed onto a rapidly rotating copper wheel. A ribbon of amorphous metal is formed.

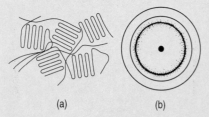

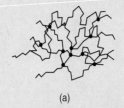

(a) (b)

Fig 2.7

To see if you have understood the way in which X-ray crystallography can tell us about the structure of solids, try to answer the following questions on the structures of polymers and of silica.

2.6 Fig 2.7(a) shows the structure of a typical long-chain polymer. In some regions, the chains are randomly oriented; in others, there is short-range order, which extends over 10–20 molecules. Fig 2.7(b) shows the X-ray diffraction pattern for such a polymer. Can you explain how these two pictures are related?

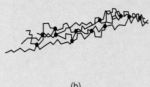
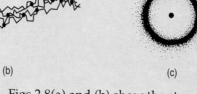
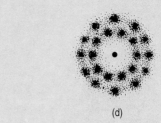

(a) (b) (c) (d)

Fig 2.8 **(a, b)** The molecular arrangement in rubber becomes more ordered when it is stretched.
(c, d) The corresponding X-ray diffraction patterns, but which is which? (See question 2.8.)

2.7 Figs 2.8(a) and (b) show the structure of a rubber band, unstretched and then stretched. When it is unstretched, the molecules are very disordered. When it is stretched, the molecules are pulled so that they tend to line up along the length of the band. Figs 2.8(c) and (d) show the corresponding X-ray diffraction patterns, but which is which?

2.8 A single crystal of quartz (silica SiO_2) is crushed into a powder; it is then melted and cooled to form a glass. It is examined using X-ray crystallography at all stages of the procedure (crystal, powder, liquid, glass). Describe the X-ray patterns you would expect to see, and explain how they relate to the structure of the material.

2.2 THE STRUCTURE OF CRYSTALLINE MATERIALS

Many solids (including ionic solids and metals) are built from an ordered array of spherical ions. We will adopt a very simple model to investigate how these ions may be arranged in the solid. We imagine that the particles are identical hard spheres that attract each other. (We have already discussed the origins of these attractive forces. The hardness of the spheres represents the short-range repulsive forces between the particles.)

INVESTIGATION

Fig 2.9

To see how such spheres can pack together, try the following investigations. Use 5 cm diameter polystyrene spheres.

A close-packed structure
Lay out a 5×4 array of spheres inside a rectangular fence 25 cm × 20 cm (Fig 2.9). They form an array of squares. Now stack a 4×3 array on top, in the spaces between the spheres of the first layer. Add two more layers to form a pyramid. Notice that the sloping faces of the pyramid have spheres closely packed in a hexagonal array.

Count the number of spheres that are in contact with each sphere in the square array. How many surround each sphere in the hexagonal array? Within this ordered structure you should find some planes that are closely packed and others that are less closely packed.

What you have observed is **anisotropy** within a crystalline structure – the arrangements of atoms are different in different directions and in

Fig 2.10

different planes. This can have important consequences for its physical properties – strength, electrical and thermal conductivity, or ease of magnetisation may be different in different directions.

Coordination number

Make a triangular, close-packed layer of 15 spheres, held in place by a surrounding fence (Fig 2.10). Build another layer of 10 spheres on top. Include a coloured sphere in the centre.

How many spheres are in contact with this marker sphere in the horizontal plane? How many spheres in the plane below are touching it? Add another layer. How many spheres in this layer are touching the marker? How many altogether are touching it?

This number is called the **coordination number** of the sphere – the number of nearest neighbours in contact with it. Spheres in close-packed structures have the highest possible coordination number of 12.

Unit cell

Any regular structure can be thought of as being built up from an arrangement of particles, which is repeated throughout space. This structural unit is called a **unit cell**. A crystal is built up by repeating unit cells, in the same way as a fabric or wallpaper pattern is built by repeating a basic element of the design.

Hexagonal and cubic close packing

Look at a raft of close-packed spheres – Fig 2.11. Each sphere has six nearest neighbours. These rafts can be stacked in different ways – Fig 2.12.

The stacking arrangements are described as ABAB in Fig 2.12(a), and as ABCABC in Fig 2.12(b). The first gives the **hexagonal close-packed** (hcp) structure. The second gives the **cubic close-packed** (ccp) structure. Try to make both of these structures using rafts of spheres that have been glued together. It is relatively easy to see the repeating hexagonal unit cell within the hexagonal close-packed arrangement – Figs 2.12(c) and (d).

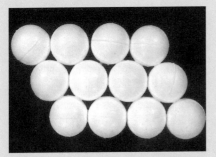

Fig 2.11 A single raft of close-packed spheres.

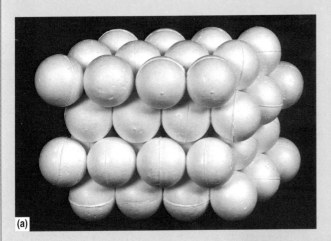

Fig 2.12 (a, b) Two ways of stacking rafts of close-packed spheres: **(a)** ABAB is hcp and **(b)** ABCABC is ccp.
(c) An hcp unit cell marked with dotted lines. **(d)** The unit cell has six atoms: one-sixth of an atom at each of the twelve corners, half an atom in each of the top and bottom faces, and a total of three atoms in the vertical faces.

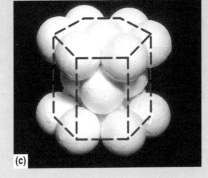

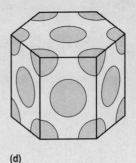

You may be able to identify the **face-centred cubic** (fcc) arrangement within the cubic close-packed array with the help of Figs 2.13(a), (b) and (c). The fcc (ccp) unit cell is shown in Figs 2.13(d) and (e).

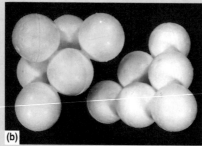

Fig 2.13 A ccp structure may be constructed from fourteen spheres.
(a) Six spheres form a triangle, with a seventh on top. **(b)** Two such arrangements, held slightly apart.
(c) When pushed together, these form a 'face-centred' cube. **(d)** A fcc unit cell marked with dotted lines.
(e) The fcc unit cell has four atoms: half an atom in each face and one-eighth of an atom at each corner.

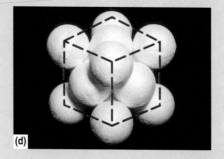
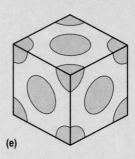

A more open structure

Another regular structure may be constructed as follows:

On a sheet of graph paper, mark a 4×4 square grid of dots 5.8 cm apart. On each spot, stick a small piece of Blu-tak. Press a 5 cm sphere firmly onto each spot – Fig 2.14(a). Build a fence around the perimeter, and then build up a pyramid of spheres.

The structure you have built is called **body-centred cubic** (bcc). The unit cell is shown in Figs 2.14(b) and (c). You can find the coordination number of this structure as follows: rebuild the pyramid gradually, with a coloured sphere in the middle of the second layer.

How many spheres of the first layer are touching the marker? How many of its own layer? How many of the layer above? What is its coordination number?

This is clearly a more open structure than the two previously described. It does not have planes of such closely packed spheres. Each sphere is in contact with eight others.

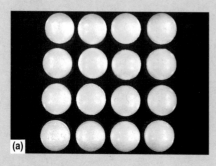
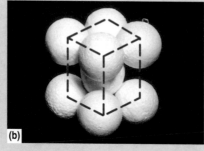
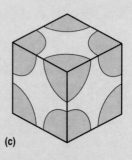

Fig 2.14 A body-centred cubic structure. **(a)** The array of spheres forming the base of the cube. **(b)** A bcc unit cell marked with dotted lines.
(c) The unit cell has two atoms: the 'body-centre' atom at the centre of the cube, and one-eighth of an atom at each corner.

PACKING PARTICLES

You should now appreciate that there are different ways of packing spheres together to represent a crystalline solid. Answer the following questions, using the knowledge you have gained from the investigation.

2.9 Some crystal structures are denser than others. Which are the most close-packed of the structures (hcp, ccp and bcc) that you have considered?

2.10 Crystalline structures are not isotropic – the atoms are not equally spaced in all directions. For the hexagonal close-packed structure, sketch a plane in which the atoms are most closely packed. How many atoms surround an individual atom in this plane? How many atoms altogether are in contact with this atom?

Metal structures

All three structures that you have built are found in metals. Soft (ductile) metals such as zinc and cadmium have hexagonal close-packed (hcp) structures, in which there are more slip planes. Copper and aluminium have cubic close-packed (ccp) structures. Body-centred cubic (bcc) arrangements of particles are found in sodium and potassium, and in iron at room temperature.

Cleavage

What other evidence do we have that the atoms or molecules that make up many solids are really arranged in a regular crystalline fashion? Some materials do form crystals with characteristic shapes that reflect the way in which their particles are arranged in planes – see Fig 2.15. However, when looked at superficially, it is not at all obvious that many of the materials that surround us are in fact crystalline.

One piece of evidence for the underlying crystalline nature of many solids is the way in which they break or **cleave**, to reveal smooth flat faces.

Cleavage shows that some planes of atoms within a crystal are less strongly bound together than are the atoms within a plane. Many ionic solids, such as potassium chloride and calcite, are found to break preferentially on certain planes. (You can try this with a razor blade and light hammer.)

Fig 2.15 Mineral crystals often have characteristic shapes that reflect the way their particles are arranged in planes.

ASSIGNMENT

Hazard warning
Take care when using a razor blade in these experiments.

Graphite is a familiar material that shows cleavage. Look at some graphite crystals under a hand lens or microscope. (The 'lead' of a 6B pencil is almost pure graphite.) Try to cleave the crystals with a razor blade or pen-knife. The carbon atoms that form the graphite are arranged in flat planes. They are bound together within the planes by covalent bonds. The planes are held together by van der Waals bonds. You should be able to see how the crystals, and the way they cleave, reflect the underlying structure. The planes of atoms can slide easily over each other – this is why graphite is useful for pencils and as a lubricant.

Real solids

Of course, we have only considered a simple model for the constituent particles of solids. We already know that many molecules and indeed many solids are held together by covalent bonds. These are strong, directional bonds, and so we would not expect the spherical particle model to apply.

Which materials might we expect to behave as predicted by our simple model of hard, spherical particles?

Pure metals consist of many identical roughly spherical atoms, and these behave most like hard spheres. Ionic solids are more complex, since they usually consist of ions of different shapes and sizes. Long-chain polymers might be expected to be the most difficult to pack in a regular crystalline array.

2.3 MICROSTRUCTURE OF POLYMERS

We will now consider how polymer molecules pack together. Here we will be concerned with structural arrangements on a larger scale than the atomic level considered with crystalline materials. Polymers can never be entirely crystalline. The elements of structure are tens of thousands of atoms arranged in chains; the structural features are revealed by optical and electron microscopes. We are therefore looking at the **microstructure**, not the atomic structure, of the material.

Thermoplastic polymers

Polyethene, which we know by its tradename of polythene, has a simple chemical structure (as polymers go). In its simplest form it is a long chain of repeating C_2H_4 units – Fig 2.16. Its solidification provides a model for understanding other polymeric materials. Various grades of polyethene are available commercially. They are specified according to the density of the solid.

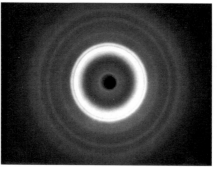
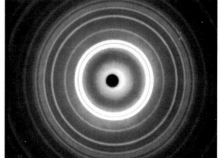

Fig 2.17 X-ray diffraction patterns for **(a)** low-density and **(b)** high-density polyethene.

Fig 2.17 shows the X-ray diffraction patterns for (a) low-density and (b) high-density forms of polyethene.

Remember that density changes in a specific material reflect different ways of packing the particles, so the X-ray patterns can provide information about the structure of polyethene in these two forms.

Both patterns have diffuse rings indicating an amorphous phase. The sharp rings, characteristic of a polycrystalline material, are more intense for high-density polyethene, indicating that it contains a higher proportion of crystalline materials.

We need to consider the detailed structure of the molecular chains to understand why the high-density material has crystallinity. A single linear chain would result if the polymerisation process occurs by simply adding basic C_2H_4 building blocks step by step, one after another at the end of a growing chain. A single such chain would be very flexible, rather like a piece of cooked spaghetti, with perhaps as many as 10^4 repeat units. The flexibility comes about because adjacent sections of the molecule can rotate about the covalent bonds that join them. Think about how such chains might pack together.

Is it likely that large numbers of entire chains would adopt perfectly

Fig 2.16 Polyethene chain.

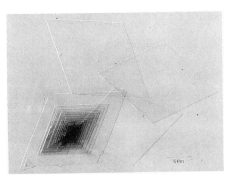

Fig 2.18 Electron micrograph of polyethene crystals grown from solution.

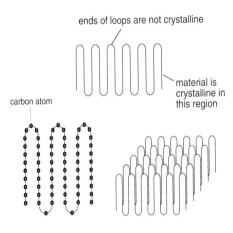

Fig 2.19 Lamella formation.

ends of loops are not crystalline

carbon atom

material is crystalline in this region

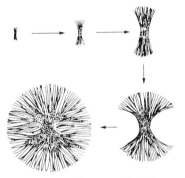

Fig 2.20 Spokes of lamellae assembling to form a spherulite.

straight arrangements and form bundles, like spaghetti is packaged when you buy it? Clearly, cooked spaghetti does not behave like this, so why should long-chain flexible molecules?

Electron microscopy of polymer crystals grown from solution (Fig 2.18) helps to unravel the problem. Isolated diamond-shaped crystalline plates 10–20 nm thick are known to consist of folded chains – Fig 2.19. A block of folded chains with about five carbon atoms in each bend makes up the ordered regions. Such an arrangement is not fully crystalline because the folds at the top and bottom of the block are not regularly packed. But the parallel rows do constitute a crystalline region. Blocks of this crystalline material are known as **lamellae**. Crystals are built up by lamellae growing in contact with one another.

Examination of thin translucent polyethene film using an optical microscope reveals a microstructure that is granular. Polarised light helps further to reveal details. The grains are called **spherulites**. If they could grow in isolation, they would become spherical. However, they stop growing when they come into contact with neighbouring spherulites, resulting in an equiaxed structure that resembles a polycrystalline metal. Spokes consisting of stacks of lamellae radiate from the centre – Fig 2.20. Regions between the spokes are amorphous.

The milky appearance of polyethene is consistent with a two-phase structure. The amorphous material is less dense and has a lower refractive index than the crystalline regions. Light is reflected whenever there is a change of refractive index. There are thus many points within the material that scatter light and the material appears translucent. It becomes more opaque as its degree of crystallinity increases. On melting, translucent polyethene becomes a perfectly clear liquid; the crystalline regions have disappeared. The proportions of the amorphous and crystalline phases in the solid depend on the cooling conditions. Rapid cooling does not allow sufficient time for the development of lamellae. Large spherulites are encouraged by maintaining the temperature of the cooling solid a few degrees below the melting temperature.

Let us return to low-density polyethene. It is clear from the X-ray evidence that chains do not pack in such an orderly way. In fact, they are not single straight chains as described for the high-density material. The chains develop branches as polymerisation proceeds, and this prevents regular packing and the formation of lamellae, favouring an amorphous structure.

Nylon is another example of a generally semicrystalline polymer; perspex is usually amorphous.

| **QUESTION** | 2.11 | Other polymers are similar to polyethene. By changing a hydrogen atom for another group (though this cannot be done directly), other materials result. One of these is polystyrene. A hydrogen atom is replaced by the massive planar C_6H_5 phenyl group (Fig 2.21). What effect would you expect this to have on the formation of regularly folding chains? How would this affect the nature of the solid? |

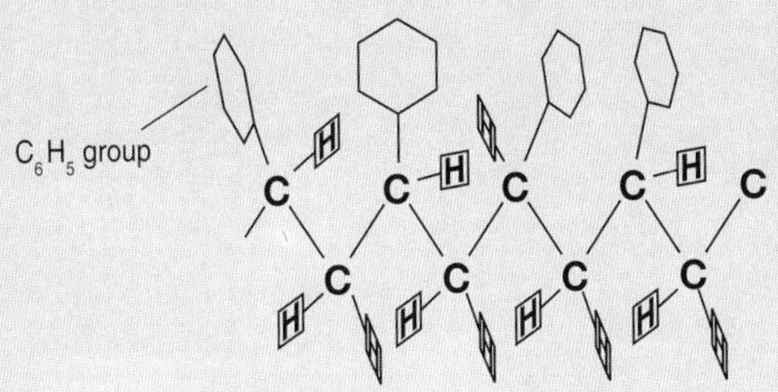

C_6H_5 group

Fig 2.21 Part of a molecular chain of polystyrene.

Thermoset polymers

Molecules in these materials are highly crosslinked by covalent bonds into a rigid three-dimensional network. Because of this structure, they do not soften on heating and usually decompose before melting. Examples of these materials are bakelite and melamine used to make electrical fittings such as light-bulb holders and switch housings – Fig 2.22.

Fig 2.22 Electrical fittings made from thermosetting polymers.

2.4 DEFECTS IN CRYSTALS

In crystals, the particles have a regular arrangement, which extends over distances of thousands of particle diameters. Such long-range order characterises crystalline materials.

Our model of a crystalline solid, based on a close-packed arrangement of hard spheres, does not show some important features of a real crystal.

First, the dimensions of the model range over only a few particle diameters. It therefore represents only a tiny part of a real crystal.

Secondly, the spheres were deliberately placed in specific arrangements to give perfect arrays. When real crystals form, there are **defects**, which result from imperfect packing and the inclusion of foreign particles in the crystal.

We will now look at some other analogues (models) of crystal structures to see how these defects arise.

Bubble rafts

This analogue uses soap bubbles, which pack together to give an orderly arrangement. The bubbles float in a raft on the surface of water; this is only a two-dimensional representation of atoms in a crystal. However, it can show other defects that are not represented in the previous model.

INVESTIGATION

Soap bubbles make a good model of a two-dimensional layer of atoms. Large numbers of bubbles of a uniform size can easily be made. They are held together by the attractive forces of surface tension; the pressure of the gas inside them stops them from collapsing and provides a repulsive force.

Setting up a bubble raft
A suitable bubble solution is made from one part of washing-up liquid, eight parts of glycerine and 32 parts of water.

Connect the rubber tubing to a gas tap (Fig 2.23). The size of the bubbles depends on both the rate of flow of the gas and how deep the needle is in the solution. Adjust the clip to control the gas flow. For best results you should aim to make bubbles of 1 mm to 2 mm diameter.

Prevent bubbles from piling up into more than one layer by wafting them away from the needle with a spatula. Wrongly sized bubbles can be burst with a hot wire and the whole raft cleared by playing a lit Bunsen burner over it. With a little practice you will soon find that you can produce a good raft.

A white surface underneath the dish and some side illumination help

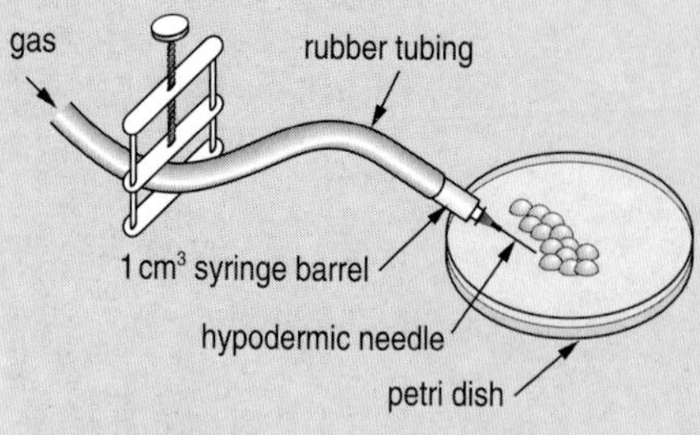

Fig 2.23 Arrangement for producing bubble rafts.

gas
rubber tubing
1 cm³ syringe barrel
hypodermic needle
petri dish

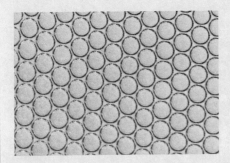

Fig 2.24

to make the effects easier to see, or you can place the dish on an overhead projector.

A regular array
Look at your bubble raft. It helps to lower your eye level and look along the rows of bubbles. Is it a perfectly ordered close-packed arrangement like the one shown in Fig 2.24?

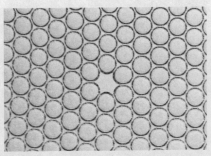

Fig 2.25

Fig 2.26

Point defects
Look at Figs 2.25 and 2.26. These are single-atom faults. Try to find similar irregularities on your raft. You can produce a defect like that shown in Fig 2.25 by bursting a bubble with a hot wire. You should be able to devise a method of introducing the fault shown in Fig 2.26. Make sure you can produce these faults in your raft if they are absent.

Dislocations
The fault shown in Fig 2.27 is much more difficult to spot; it is known as a dislocation. Tilt the page, hold it close to your eye and look carefully along the rows of bubbles. Some lines have been drawn along the bubble rows on Fig 2.28, which is the same photograph as Fig 2.27. Notice how the lines of bubbles are distorted in the region of the dislocation.

Grain boundaries
Can you pick out grain boundaries in your raft? These are boundaries between adjacent areas in which the lines of atoms run in different directions.

Moving dislocations
Use L-shaped pieces of wire to compress and stretch the raft. Look at what happens to a dislocation. You may need to try this several times to observe the effect. Make a note of what you see. What action on a crystal would have the same effect as the wires have on the raft?

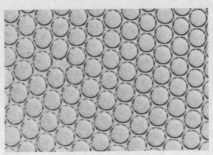

Fig 2.27

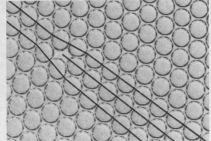

Fig 2.28

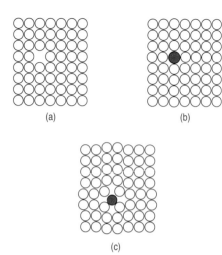

(a)   (b)

(c)

Fig 2.29 Point defects in a solid: **(a)** vacancy, **(b)** substitutional and **(c)** interstitial.

Point defects

Irregularities that are found at single points in a structure are known as point defects; there are three types, as shown in Fig 2.29.

(a) If an atom is missing at a point in the structure, we have a **vacancy**. Vacancies may arise because of imperfect packing when the solid is formed; they also arise as a result of diffusion of particles through the crystal. The number of vacancies in the crystal increases with increasing temperature, as the thermal vibration of the particles increases.

(b) All materials contain a large number of impurity atoms. If a foreign atom occupies a position within the regular array, we have a **substitutional defect**. These are usually a different size from the other atoms, and result in a disruption or distortion of the crystal regularity. Such defects are present in all materials to some degree; they are deliberately introduced into alloys and doped semiconductors to modify the properties of the material.

(c) An atom (of host or impurity) may be squeezed in between the atoms of the normal array in a perfect crystal. This is known as an **interstitial defect**. This can arise when an atom diffuses from an occupied position into an interstitial site, leaving behind a vacancy. Particles of materials added during alloying may also occupy interstitial sites.

Line defects

These are usually called **dislocations**, of which there are various types. In an edge dislocation, an extra half-plane of atoms appears in the crystal. This is represented in the bubble raft model by an extra half-row of bubbles (Fig 2.27).

Ball-bearing model

This consists of a single layer of many identical ball-bearings, which can move freely within a plastic frame. Shaking the frame causes the ball-bearings to rearrange. Fig 2.30 shows a typical picture of the frame after shaking.

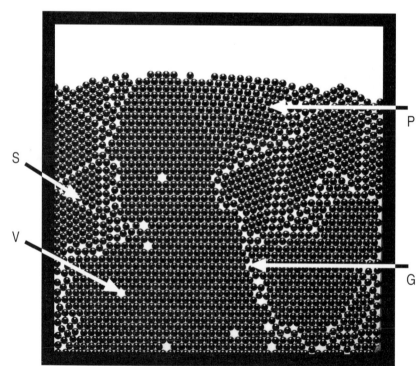

Fig 2.30 A ball-bearing model of crystal structure. Several 'grains' of different orientations can be identified. *Key:* G = grain boundary, S = slip plane, V = vacancy, P = low packing density.

A single crystal (perfect array) never forms. You can see instead that the balls pack to form a number of smaller 'crystals' or 'crystallites'. Each is represented by parallel rows of balls, but the orientation of the rows changes from one crystallite to the next. In a real solid, the individual crystallites are known as **grains**, and the regions between them are **grain boundaries**. There is considerable disorder in the boundary regions, which can extend over distances of several particle diameters.

Other defects that are conspicuous in the ball-bearing analogue are vacancies and **slip planes**. The latter result from a small relative movement of two parts of a crystal.

It is difficult for dislocations to form in this model because ball-bearings, unlike atoms, are not deformable and do not attract one another. (Sometimes slip planes are mistakenly identified as dislocations in this model.) Regions of low-density packing can sometimes be seen near the unbounded surface; these are not seen in real metals, and illustrate that the model is imperfect.

It is important to realise that both line defects and grain boundaries are three-dimensional defects in real crystals. Grain boundaries and slip planes are classified as **planar defects**.

ASSIGNMENT

If you have one of these ball-bearing models, experiment with it. You should be able to see other irregularities in the packing of the ball-bearings. (You can make similar models by putting a single layer of lentils or grains of rice in a Petri dish.)

Evidence of dislocations

Single crystals of very pure materials can be grown free from grain boundaries and substitutional defects. However, in even the best single crystals of silicon or germanium used in semiconductor technology, there may be as many as one million dislocations per square metre, i.e. one line crossing every $1\,mm^2$. In more typical metal samples, there may be very extensive dislocations, as much as $10^4\,km$ of line dislocation in $1\,mm^3$. This is an indication of just how imperfect most crystalline materials are.

Electron microscopy provides direct evidence of dislocations. A beam of electrons is focused onto a thin specimen to produce an image in a similar way to light passing through a transparent material. Dislocations show up as dark lines passing through the specimen from one surface to the other (Fig 2.31), rather like fine cracks in a pane of glass.

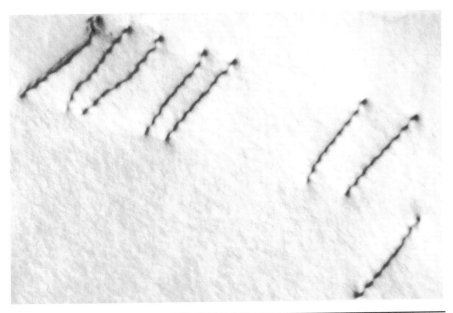

Fig 2.31 Dislocations passing through a thin metal foil; magnification 50 000×.

2.12 Explain why solids generally expand as the temperature increases. (One reason is to do with interatomic forces; the other is to do with lattice defects.)

In questions 2.13 and 2.14 below, which of the three statements is/are correct? In each case, explain your answer.

2.13 A hexagonal close-packed structure of identical spherical particles is characterised by:

(a) a coordination number of 8,

(b) a body-centred cubic unit cell,

(c) the minimum fraction of unfilled space.

2.14 An edge dislocation in a solid may be described as:

(a) a small crack,

(b) a fault in the packing of the atoms,

(c) the boundary between two crystallites.

SUMMARY

The structure of materials may be investigated in a number of ways. X-ray and electron diffraction patterns give information about the arrangements of particles and their separations.

A study of the packing of spherical particles shows that they may be packed in different ways, with different degrees of closeness of packing. These represent idealised structures of materials. In practice, the particles of which real materials are made are not perfectly spherical. Covalently bonded molecules can be far from spherical, and polymer molecules may be very long, flexible chains. The structures of real materials are likely to have a range of defects, classified as point, line and planar defects.

Chapter 3

CONTROLLING MICROSTRUCTURE

The physical properties of materials, which are of vital importance to engineers, depend on the **microstructure**; that is, the arrangement of grains and phases as seen under the microscope. Change the microstructure and you change the properties. Thus, a knowledge of how to control or design the microstructure of materials is an important tool for materials scientists and engineers.

LEARNING OBJECTIVES

After studying this chapter you should be able to:

1. describe the range of solid structures that may be formed from a liquid in terms of their degree of disorder;

2. describe how the microstructure of a solid can be modified by the following processes: crosslinking, devitrification, heat treatment, sintering and working;

3. use correctly the following scientific terms: 'annealing' and 'alloying'.

3.1 MICROSTRUCTURE AS HISTORY

If an engineer wishes to know why a particular machine or construction has failed, a materials scientist may be called on to investigate the materials used. These investigations will include looking at the microstructure of the materials.

The microstructure that we observe represents the history of the material – it is a record of what happened during the processes of solidification, forming, heating, cooling, working and so on that the material has experienced. In order to see how the material may behave in use, the materials scientist must interpret this record.

Typically a solid is formed by cooling a liquid. The resulting structure is then modified by appropriate treatment. Fig 3.1 illustrates the various routes that may be followed in forming a solid with the desired microstructure and properties. By the end of this chapter, you should understand the different terms used in this diagram.

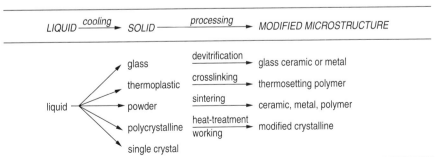

Fig 3.1 Different microstructures are achieved by different rates of cooling and different processing of the solid that results.

Solidification

The formation of a solid from a liquid is not an instantaneous process. The structure that results depends on the conditions of cooling, and in particular on the rate of cooling.

Rapid cooling may result in an **amorphous** structure. The particles of the liquid do not have time to rearrange into an ordered, crystalline structure. The relatively disordered liquid structure is retained in the solid, although this is an unstable situation.

The opposite extreme may be achieved by carefully controlled slow cooling to give a **single crystal**. This is the most ordered structure possible. Single crystals of silicon, Si, are very important in the electronics industry. Fig 3.2 shows a large crystal being grown. The silicon used has extremely high purity (less than one part per billion of impurities), and the crystal structure is very regular. Thin slices will be cut from this crystal as the basis for manufacturing electronic chips.

Silica, SiO_2, is a familiar substance that shows these extremes. Window glass consists largely of silica in an amorphous state, formed by rapid cooling. In Nature, large crystals of quartz are found that have formed by the slow cooling of molten silica over long periods of time. In practice, most materials form solids between these limits.

Thermoplastic polymers, as we have discussed in Section 2.3, may solidify to give microcrystalline regions where the hydrocarbon chains are closely aligned, surrounded by amorphous regions of disordered chains.

Other materials form polycrystalline solids. The atoms, ions or molecules form ordered structures – **grains** – surrounded by regions of disorder – **grain boundaries**.

Metals are generally polycrystalline. When a mixture of molten metals solidifies, there are several possible outcomes. The different atoms may be completely mixed to give a solid of uniform composition, called a **solid solution**. This is referred to as a **single phase**. More usually, two or more phases may result. Different regions of the solid have different compositions. Elements may combine to form compounds, which may then segregate from the rest of the metal to form a **second phase**. The outcome is a polycrystalline solid with grains of different chemical compositions.

Similarly, any other mixture of materials may solidify in this way. Many of the rocks around us are polycrystalline, having formed from a melt containing several different substances – for example, the granite shown in Fig 3.3.

The investigations that follow are concerned with the formation of a solid from a liquid. The formation of many solids is similar, but may not always be easy to observe directly. The first two investigations use model systems to show some of the processes that occur during solidification. The third investigation shows how control of the cooling rate of a liquid metal can affect its microstructure.

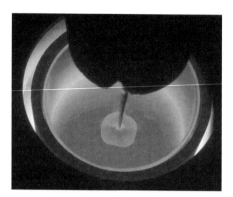

Fig 3.2 A large single crystal of silicon being manufactured. This crystal will form the basis of thousands of electronic chips.

Fig 3.3 This sample of granite shows the presence of different crystalline regions – it is polycrystalline.

INVESTIGATION

Dendrite formation

When a liquid cools and solidifies, crystal growth starts – is nucleated – at many points in the liquid. The solid crystal gradually extends into the liquid, often in the form of branching, tree-like 'dendrites'. Eventually the solid regions begin to touch. Each dendrite results in a crystallite or grain; where the crystallites touch is a grain boundary. Fig 3.4 illustrates this process.

Clean a few copper filings in some dilute nitric acid. Using a dropping pipette, put a few drops of 0.05 M silver nitrate solution on a microscope slide. Add a single copper filing to the solution, and focus the microscope on it. You should see dendrites of silver growing outwards from the copper. Over the next few minutes, you should be able to observe the way in which the dendrites grow, branch and interlock.

(a)

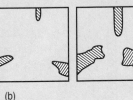
(b)

Fig 3.4 **(a)** Crystalline dendrites form as a liquid cools. **(b)** Each dendrite forms the nucleus of a grain. The grains eventually run into one another.

INVESTIGATION

Growth of grains

Phenyl salicylate (phenyl-2-hydroxybenzoate) is a white, waxy solid at room temperature. It crystallises in a similar way to a metal but is transparent in the form of a thin film.

Warm the two pieces of glass, each about 6 cm square, by placing them in an oven at 50 °C for about 15 min. Warm the phenyl salicylate gently in the test tube until it just melts. (Its melting point is about 43 °C.) Pour a few drops of the liquid onto one of the warm glass plates. Lower the second glass plate on top of the first so that a thin film of liquid spreads out evenly between the plates. Observe the growth of crystals as the glass plates cool.

In this investigation, you should be able to see nucleation of crystals (solidification starts at several points in the liquid) and their subsequent growth. Eventually, the crystals run into one another, and straight-line boundaries form between them.

INVESTIGATION

Hazard warning
Remember that molten metals can be dangerous. Eye protection, heat-resistant gloves and a lab-coat should be worn. The experiment should be carried out in a fume cupboard.

Grains in a zinc ingot

The shape of the crystals that are formed when a metal solidifies depends on two quantities: the rate of cooling and the temperature gradient within the liquid. In this experiment you will observe the effect of cooling conditions on the grain structure of zinc.

Melt approx 60 g of zinc by heating it in a pyrex tube. Granulated zinc is easily oxidised, especially if it is heated slowly. Careful stirring of the melting mass with a wooden splint will help to break up and reduce oxide scum within the melt. Clamp the tube firmly and leave it to cool to room temperature. Remove the zinc ingot. You may have to break the tube to do this. Cut a notch around the circumference of the ingot, and about 2 cm from the rounded end, using the hacksaw. Place the ingot in the vice so that the notch is just above the jaws. Give it a sharp blow with the hammer to fracture it.

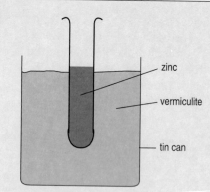

Examine the grain structure of the fracture surface using a hand lens. You can now use a slower cooling rate by placing the test tube containing the molten zinc in an insulating jacket of vermiculite. A diagram of the arrangement is shown in Fig 3.5. Put about 1 cm depth of vermiculite into the empty can. Place the test tube containing the molten zinc in the can and quickly pour the rest of the vermiculite around the test tube to fill the can. Leave the test tube to cool and examine the fracture surface again.

If you find the crystals difficult to see, you may like to try polishing and etching your specimens. A method is described in Appendix C. Fig 3.6 shows etched and polished specimens of zinc, cooled at different rates.

Fig 3.5 Slow cooling arrangement for the solidification of zinc.

Fig 3.6 Two specimens of zinc, cooled at different rates, showing the different sizes of crystals that result: **(a)** rapidly cooled and **(b)** slowly cooled.

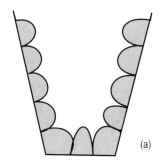 (a)

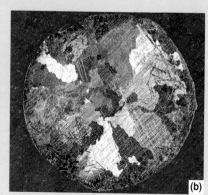 (b)

Casting metals

Many metal items are formed by casting; the molten material is poured into a mould of the desired shape. The polycrystalline microstructure of a cast metal reflects the cooling process that has occurred.

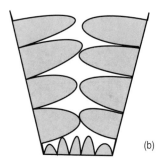

Fig 3.7 Formation and growth of crystals in a cooling cast.

Liquid that is closest to the mould walls cools rapidly and 'chill crystals' are formed – Fig 3.7(a). These crystals continue to grow into the body of the liquid, giving long 'columnar crystals' – Fig 3.7(b). Nucleation centres may be present throughout the liquid and crystal growth may begin within it when it cools to or below the freezing point. Crystals initiated in the bulk of the liquid grow equally in all directions; they are 'equiaxed'. The actual grain structure formed may have both types of crystal (Fig 3.7(c)) and depends on the ratio:

(temperature gradient through the liquid)/(overall cooling rate)

A high ratio favours a high proportion of columnar crystals.

Fig 3.8 shows an as-cast structure for a polished and etched aluminium ingot. Both types of grains are clearly visible.

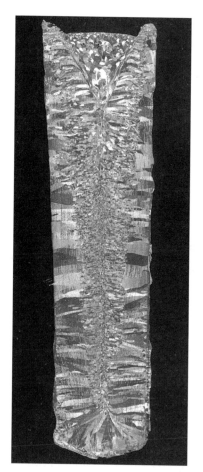

Fig 3.8 Crystals in an aluminium ingot.

CONTROLLING MICROSTRUCTURE

3.1 Study the photograph of the microstructure of the cast aluminium ingot – Fig 3.8. Which crystals are columnar, and which are equiaxed? Draw two sketches of the ingot to show how you think it might have looked:

(a) when only 10% of the metal had solidified,

(b) when 50% had solidified.

3.2 If you made zinc ingots, you may have noticed that they had a hole down the centre. This is called a 'pipe'. (You can see a pipe in the photograph of the aluminium ingot – Fig 3.8.) Explain how this may be formed.

3.2 PROCESSING MATERIALS

We will now look at the various processes that may be used to treat a solid to achieve a desired microstructure.

It would be wrong to think of the particles that make up a solid as having rigidly fixed positions. Rather, some degree of motion is always possible. At temperatures approaching the melting point, particle motion increases dramatically. The presence of defects in the structure is of vital importance. Ions may migrate by way of vacancies in the crystal. Particles may travel along grain boundaries. Dislocations migrate through the crystal. Material may diffuse between neighbouring grains, causing them to grow or shrink.

This motion on the atomic level allows us to change the microstructure of a solid without remelting it.

Devitrification

Glasses are formed because particles have insufficient time to arrange in the orderly way associated with true solids. An ordered arrangement has lower energy and is more stable. Heat treatment of a glass can allow the particles increased freedom of movement, so that crystals can form in the material. This process is called **devitrification**.

An important group of strong polycrystalline materials known as **glass ceramics** is made in this way. A nucleating agent, such as zirconium dioxide or titanium dioxide, is added to the glass constituents. The materials are melted to make a glass, which is then formed into the item required. It is then held at a temperature below its softening point for a controlled period of time. During this time the nucleating agent initiates formation of crystals, which grow in a very uniform manner throughout the material. By careful selection of the composition of the parent glass and control of the heat treatment, microstructure can be controlled to produce a greater range of materials tailor-made for specific applications.

Materials that are transparent have crystals that are smaller than the wavelength of light. As crystal size increases, the materials look less like glass and become opaque. The uniform size of the crystals confers strength and resistance to sudden changes of temperature (thermal shock). These properties make ceramic glasses suitable for manufacturing tableware with a guaranteed resistance to breakage and cooking utensils that can be placed directly on red-hot heating elements.

Fig 3.9 shows the uniform grain size that may be achieved in these materials.

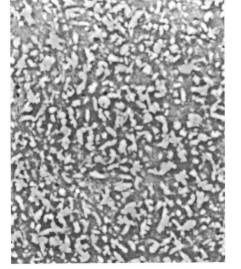

Fig 3.9 Microstructure of a glass ceramic.

Crosslinking

Thermoplastic polymers can be melted and moulded into any desired shape. If the material is subjected to heating after moulding, it may deform because the polymer chains become free to move. The rigidity and strength

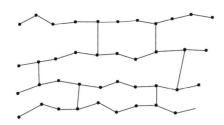

Fig 3.10 Crosslinks in a linear polymer.

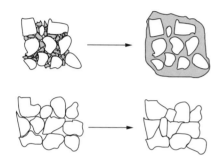

Fig 3.11 (a) Vitrification and **(b)** sintering.

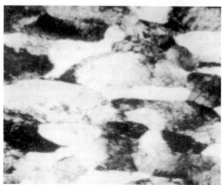

Fig 3.12 The microstructure of aluminium
specimens:
(a) annealed condition before rolling;
(b) after rolling.

of a component can be increased by inhibiting chain movement, by forming new links between neighbouring chains. This is known as **crosslinking** and is illustrated schematically in Fig 3.10. A structure that originally consisted of individual chains held together by weak bonds is transformed into a three-dimensional network with strong bonds holding the chains rigidly together.

Crosslinking involves chemical reactions, and there are a number of ways in which this may be achieved. Natural rubber may be crosslinked using sulphur. The process in this case is known as **vulcanising**. Car tyres have a sulphur content between 3 and 5%. Adding more sulphur increases the extent of crosslinking and the rigidity of the material. Some car battery cases are made from vulcanised rubber, but in these the sulphur content may be as high as 40%, resulting in a rigid brittle material.

Solids from powders

Solids are not always formed from the melt. Their melting point may be impractically high, or we may wish to achieve a structure that is porous or of low density. In such cases, we may form an object from a powder of small grains. The powder may be made solid in different ways, as shown in Fig 3.11.

Vitrification

The powder contains grains of different materials. It is heated so that one material melts and forms a liquid, which, on cooling, becomes a glass that holds the solid together. Vitrification occurs in the firing of clay ceramics, e.g. in brick and china manufacture.

Sintering

The compacted powder is heated to a temperature below its melting point. The material changes to a dense, strong polycrystalline material. This comes about through a movement of matter to fill the interstices between the powder particles. At high temperatures, the atoms have sufficient mobility to migrate via vacancies in the crystal.

Sintering, which may be aided by applying pressure (known as 'hot pressing'), is used in the forming of many ceramic and metal objects. Ferrite magnets are made in this way, as are porous bronze bearings, which are both absorbent and hard, and so can be soaked in oil to give a long service life.

Working and heat treatment

If a ductile polycrystalline material is hammered or rolled or otherwise mechanically deformed, this is known as **working**. If this is done to a cold metal, it becomes harder and more brittle. Large numbers of dislocations are introduced into the metal; the crystal structure is very strained.

This is another example of an unstable structure. Work has been done to give strain energy to the metal. If the temperature of the metal is raised above $(0.4–0.5) \times T_m$ (where T_m is its melting point in kelvins (K)), the increased thermal motion of the atoms allows a rearrangement of the crystal structure. A process called **recrystallisation** takes place, in which new strain-free grains grow at the expense of the strained grains. Grain boundaries of these new grains sweep through the metal, replacing the work-hardened grains by a new set of more perfect grains. This form of heat treatment is sometimes called **annealing**. The metal becomes softer and more ductile.

Fig 3.12 shows the microstructure of a metal and how it changes during working and annealing. In Chapter 5 we will look in more detail at the ways in which these treatments affect the mechanical properties of metals.

CONTROLLING MICROSTRUCTURE

3.3 Which of the following statements about the structures of materials is/are correct? Explain your answers.

(a) When a solid melts, the average separation of the particles of which it is composed increases.

(b) In a solid, the particles occupy fixed positions; in a liquid, they are completely free to move about throughout the liquid.

3.4 In which of the following ways do a glass and a crystalline solid of the same material differ?

(a) melting point,

(b) particle arrangement,

SUMMARY ASSIGNMENT

We have described some of the important processes used by materials scientists to achieve a desired microstructure. It is useful to know some of the terms commonly used to describe these processes. Make a glossary of such terms, by referring to some of the recommended books, or use a scientific or technical dictionary. Include 'devitrification', 'crosslinking', 'sintering', 'working', 'annealing', 'alloying'. Try to include examples of products made using these processes, and explain why their structure makes them suitable for these uses.

The effects of these processes on the physical properties of materials can be very dramatic, and are discussed in the chapters that follow.

SUMMARY

The structures of solids range from perfectly crystalline to amorphous. Most materials have structures that lie between these two extremes.

The structure of a solid material depends on how it was formed. When a solid forms from a liquid, it may have a tendency to crystallise. The subsequent structure depends on the rate of cooling and the temperature gradient.

Solid materials may be processed to change their structure. A variety of processes are used in order to achieve a desired set of properties.

EXAMINATION QUESTIONS: Theme 1

T1.1

The graph shows how the force, F, between a pair of molecules varies with their separation, r.

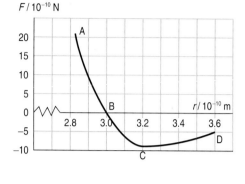

(a) Describe how F varies with r in the regions A → B, B → C and C → D.

Explain how a solid rod made of molecules which behave in this way will behave for small applied longitudinal forces.

(b) Using the information on the graph:

Write down the equilibrium separation of the molecules, and calculate the strain beyond which the intermolecular bond would break.

Estimate the energy required to decrease the separation of the molecules from 3.0×10^{-10} m to 2.9×10^{-10} m.

(ULEAC 1993)

T1.2

The sketch shows, approximately, how the resultant force between adjacent atoms in a solid depends on r, their distance apart.

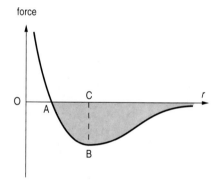

(a) Which distance on the graph represents the equilibrium separation of the atoms? Briefly justify your answer.

(b) What is the significance of the shaded area?

(c) Use the graph to explain why you would expect the solid to obey Hooke's law for *small* extensions and compressions.

(WJEC 1992)

T1.3

Nickel, relative atomic mass 58.7, crystallises in a cubic close-packed structure with a lattice parameter [length of unit cell] of 0.3516 nm at 20 °C.

(a) Sketch the structure, indicating clearly the cubic unit cell.

(b) Calculate

(i) the atomic radius of nickel

(ii) the density of a perfect nickel crystal

(c) Describe the changes you would expect in both the structure and in the X-ray diffraction pattern obtained from a specimen of polycrystalline nickel as its temperature is raised towards and through its melting point.

(NEAB 1988)

Theme 2

MECHANICAL PROPERTIES OF MATERIALS

In Theme 2, we will look at the mechanical properties of materials: how do materials respond when they are subjected to forces that stretch or compress them? All materials will deform and eventually break, but some are much stiffer than others, and some are much stronger than others. In Chapter 4, we look at *how* materials deform and break, and in Chapter 5 we consider *why* they have this behaviour. An understanding of the answers to these questions allows materials scientists to design new materials with improved mechanical properties, materials that can be used to satisfy the requirements of demanding new applications.

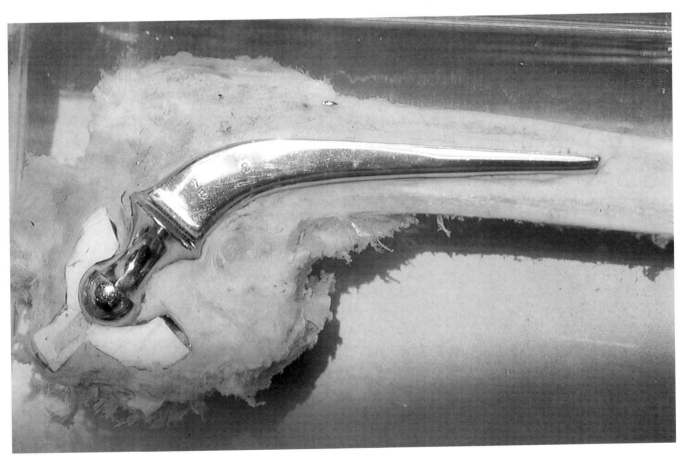

This artificial hip joint illustrates three classes of materials with important mechanical properties. The metal section is both stiff and strong. The polymer socket is both smooth and rigid, for ease of movement. Bone is a natural composite material that is light and very strong under compression. Both natural and synthetic materials must be chemically stable for long periods in an environment of body fluid.

Chapter **4**

MEASURING MECHANICAL PROPERTIES

How will a piece of material respond when subjected to forces? This is a vital question, which engineers and designers must be able to answer when they set about choosing a suitable material for a particular application. Will it stretch? Will it break? In this chapter, we look at how we can describe forces, and how we can measure their effects on materials.

LEARNING OBJECTIVES

After studying this chapter you should be able to:

1. use correctly the terms 'tension', 'compression' and 'shear';

2. use stress–strain graphs to determine the Young modulus and tensile strength of materials;

3. use correctly the terms 'elastic deformation', 'plastic deformation', 'viscoelastic deformation', 'brittleness', 'ductility', 'hardness' and 'toughness';

4. explain the distinction between stiffness and tensile strength;

5. explain the terms 'creep', 'fatigue' and 'hysteresis', and explain why these phenomena are important.

4.1 SELECTING MATERIALS

Introduction

One of the most important tasks that a materials scientist performs in industry is the selection of suitable materials for a particular use. Here is a technological problem concerning the selection of materials for you to think about:

What material would you use to make a container for fizzy drinks? Of course, as with many technological problems, there may be more than one answer. Fig 4.1 shows different solutions to the problem of containing Coca-Cola.

Fig 4.1 Plastic, glass and metal containers for Coca-Cola.

ASSIGNMENT

It is worth thinking about why there are several different solutions to the problem of containing a fizzy drink. What do we require of the material being used? What physical properties must it have? What other factors might we take into consideration?

Qualities and choices

There are no definitive answers to the questions in the assignment; you may have referred to the following qualities: strength, stiffness, rigidity, ease of breaking, density, transparency, cost, ease of fabrication, ease of disposal or recycling, resistance to corrosion, permeability, availability, how attractive it is, and so on. These are all factors that a materials scientist would have to take into account; they are all rather vague, and, if a sensible conclusion is to be arrived at, it is necessary to think very carefully about just what we mean by strength, stiffness and so on.

Many of these qualities, although of great importance, are outside the realms of physics. In this chapter we shall try to develop an insight into the mechanical properties of solids, how they depend on the microstructure of the material, and how they may be controlled for use in particular applications.

4.2 TENSION AND COMPRESSION

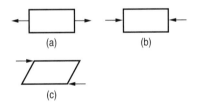

Fig 4.2 **(a)** Tensile, **(b)** compressive and **(c)** shear forces.

Stretching and compressing

The mechanical properties of a material tell us how it behaves in response to applied forces. Does it stretch? Does it bend? Does it break?

If a body is stretched, we say it is **in tension**; tensile forces have been applied. We are pulling against the attractive forces that are acting between the particles of which the body is made.

Similarly, if a body is squeezed, we say it is **in compression**; compressive forces have been applied. They push against the repulsive forces between the particles.

If two forces are applied causing the body to twist, we describe them as **shear forces** – see Fig 4.2.

A body may be partly in a state of tension, partly in compression. Look at the beam shown in Fig 4.3(a). It is supported at both ends. One surface is stretched, the other squeezed. Which is which? The lower surface is in a state of tension. If the beam were made of concrete, it might well break as shown in Fig 4.3(b). Concrete is weak in tension, but strong in compression. It breaks at a crack on the surface that is in tension. This can be avoided by including a material that is strong in tension. The concrete may be reinforced by including steel rods running along the lower side of the beam. The result is a composite material – reinforced concrete.

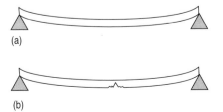

Fig 4.3 A beam is supported at both ends. It is in tension on its lower surface.

4.1 Look at the cantilever shown in Fig 4.4. This is a beam supported at one end only.

(a) Which surface is in tension?

(b) Which surface is in compression?

(c) Where would you include steel reinforcing rods if it were a concrete beam?

Fig 4.4 A cantilever is supported at one end only.

Fig 4.5 These buttresses were the mediaeval architect's way of using the compressive strength of stone to support a massive building.

Building structures

Stone has been a very important building material for thousands of years. Like concrete, it is weak in tension. However, it cannot be reinforced, so it must always be used in compression. The arch, dome and buttress (Fig 4.5) are three structures that have been devised in which stone is compressed to exploit its strength. Indeed, you may have noticed that arches are sometimes the only parts of ruined monasteries that remain standing – see Fig 4.6.

Fig 4.7 shows how the loads at various points on a bridge are converted into compressive forces on the stones. The weight of the bridge is transmitted by the arch to the abutments at either end.

Fig 4.6 A stone arch is a strong structure, able to endure for hundreds of years.

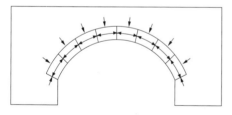

Fig 4.7 The stones that form an arch are all in a state of compression.

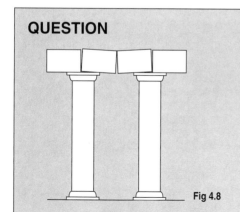

4.2 Fig 4.8 shows a classical Greek structure, over two thousand years old, in which a beam is supported by columns. The beam cracked in ancient times but is standing to this day, still capable of supporting a load. Use the idea of tensile and compressive forces to explain:

(a) why the beam cracked;

(b) why it has remained stable after cracking.

Fig 4.8

MEASURING MECHANICAL PROPERTIES

Photoelastic stress analysis

The tensile and compressive forces acting within an engineering structure may be very complex, and difficult to predict. An interesting technique – photoelastic stress analysis – is used by engineers to examine the forces present in model structures; regions of high stress can then be eliminated from a design. A typical photoelastic image is shown in Fig 4.9. How does it work?

Many transparent materials if stressed and viewed between crossed pieces of polaroid show a pattern of coloured fringes. These are known as **photoelastic materials**. The forces within the material cause very slight distortions of the arrangement of molecules within it. This alters the electric field within the material. Light is a form of electromagnetic radiation, and the distorted electric field affects the polarisation of the light as it passes through, giving rise to the pattern of coloured interference fringes.

Analysis of this pattern allows engineers to map the distribution and to calculate the magnitude of stresses in models of structures. The technique is therefore of great value to the engineer who needs to select appropriate materials that will not fail in action.

If white light is used to illuminate the model, the interference pattern consists of a series of coloured fringes known as **isochromatic lines** and black fringes known as **isoclinic lines**. Each coloured isochromatic fringe corresponds to a certain value of stress. They are similar to contour lines, which show height above sea level, on a map, except that they show points of equal stress.

Isoclinic lines show the direction of the stress within the material. If the structure is rotated between the polaroids, the isoclinic lines move. It is thus possible to determine the direction of the principal stresses at every point in the structure by rotating it and seeing how the isoclinic fringes move.

A full stress analysis of a structure is time-consuming and difficult. You can, however, see some useful qualitative effects in the investigation that follows.

Fig 4.9 A photoelastic stress image.

INVESTIGATION

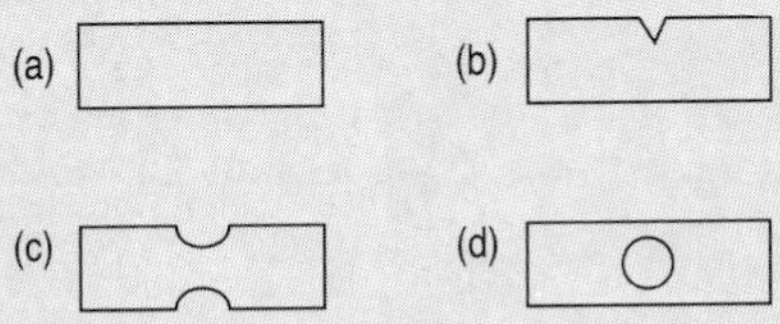

Fig 4.10

(a) (b) (c) (d)

You will need two pieces of polaroid at least 5 cm square, and some strips of heavy-gauge polyethene 4 cm wide cut as shown in Fig 4.10.

Support the pieces of polaroid so that they are vertical and arrange them to be crossed – Fig 4.11. The minimum amount of light is transmitted when they are in this position. Grip the polyethene strips at each end between two strips of wood or plastic. Place the strips between the crossed polaroids and gently pull the two ends apart. Observe the patterns that develop, particularly the places where they first appear.

A strip of thin perspex with a single cut as in Fig 4.10(b) is useful to illustrate stress concentration at the end of a crack. The stress concentration at the end of a crack illustrates the contribution of surface cracks to the reduction of the strength of a material. A material is more susceptible to fracture if there are many surface cracks that can easily propagate.

If you have a clear plastic ruler or spectacles with plastic lenses, try looking at stress patterns in these.

If your school or college has a polariscope and some models made from a suitable photoelastic material, you may like to try other experiments.

In industry, a material called Photoflex is used for making model structures, as it is a sensitive photoelastic polymeric material. It shows large changes in the pattern of fringes for small levels of stress.

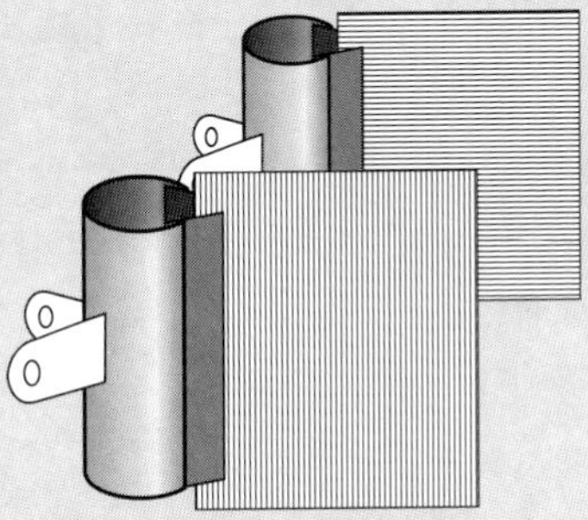

Fig 4.11 The two polaroids must be crossed.

4.3 STRESS–STRAIN CURVES

extension x

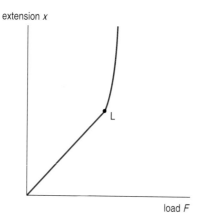

load F

Fig 4.12 Load–extension graph for a piece of material.

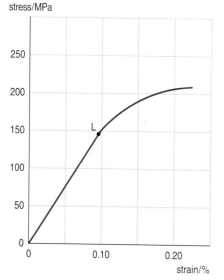

Fig 4.13 Stress–strain graph corresponding to Fig 4.12.

Table 4.1 Quantities and units in tensile testing

Quantity	Symbol	Unit
original length	l	m
extension	x	m
area	A	m^2
load	F	N
stress	σ	Pa or N m^{-2}
strain	ε	no unit or %
Young modulus	E	Pa or N m^{-2}

We have already referred to the strength and stiffness of materials. However, we have been using these terms in their everyday senses. There are several other ways of describing materials – brittle, tough, hard, ductile and so on – which are in everyday use, but which also have carefully defined meanings to a materials scientist. In the rest of this chapter, we will look carefully at how we can define these terms, and how we can measure these important mechanical properties.

Stress and strain

If we use a tensile force to stretch a piece of material, it stretches. Its length increases, and we can measure the extension x (increases in length) for different values of load F (tensile force). We might find that our results gave a load–extension graph like that shown in Fig 4.12.

This graph has an initial straight section, in which the extension is proportional to the load. In this region, the piece of material is said to obey **Hooke's law:**

$$x \propto F \quad \text{or} \quad F = kx$$

where k is the constant of proportionality, the **stiffness** of the piece of material.

Beyond point L, the graph is no longer a straight line, and Hooke's law is not obeyed.

Now, in this discussion, we have only considered a *piece* of material. But what can we say about the behaviour of the material itself? We need to eliminate the fact that we took a particular piece of material, with particular dimensions. To do this, we define two quantities related to x and F.

For a piece of material of original length l and cross-sectional area A, we define **stress** σ and **strain** ε as follows:

$$\text{stress} = \text{load}/\text{area}$$

$$\sigma = F/A$$

and

$$\text{strain} = \text{extension}/\text{original length}$$

$$\varepsilon = x/l$$

If we now plot a graph of stress against strain, we find the graph shown in Fig 4.13. Note that this curves in the opposite way to Fig 4.12, since we have reversed the axes by putting stress on the y axis. Previously, the load was on the x axis.

The gradient of the initial linear section of this graph tells us the **Young modulus** E of the material, a measure of its stiffness. This is defined by:

$$\text{Young modulus} = \text{stress}/\text{strain}$$

$$E = \sigma/\varepsilon$$

Beyond the point labelled L, the material no longer behaves according to Hooke's law. At the end of the graph, it breaks.

Table 4.1 gives a summary of the units that we shall be using in this book, and which you will need to understand in order to answer the questions.

QUESTIONS

4.3 Look at the stress–strain graph shown in Fig 4.13. Use it to deduce the following quantities:

(a) the strain produced by a stress of 20 MPa;

(b) the stress required to produce a strain of 0.05%;

(c) the Young modulus of the material.

Table 4.2 Values of Young modulus for several metals

Metal	Young modulus/GPa
aluminium	70
copper	130
iron	210
lead	16
mild steel	210

4.4 Table 4.2 shows values for the Young modulus of some metals.

(a) Which metal is the stiffest?

(b) Which is the least stiff?

(c) Why are the values for iron and steel the same?

4.5 A copper wire, 2.0 m long, is stretched by a force of 50 N. If the wire has a diameter of 1 mm, by how much will it stretch?

Tensile testing of materials

Materials engineers are involved in testing materials – tensile testing, hardness testing, impact testing, fatigue testing and so on – to determine the mechanical properties of materials and their suitability for new applications. Industrial tensile testing machines, like the one shown in Fig 4.14, are capable of applying forces of 100 kN or more.

In the investigation that follows, you will test several different materials by stretching them. The materials have been chosen to show different characteristic behaviours under tension.

Fig 4.14 This tensile testing machine is capable of applying loads of up to 100 kN.

INVESTIGATION

Hazard warning
Wear safety spectacles throughout this experiment. When a taut wire snaps, a lot of stored elastic energy is released very suddenly!

1. Stretch the wires and fibre listed in Table 4.3. Fix them horizontally along the bench as shown in Fig 4.15, with a sellotape marker and scale. The total length from A to the pulley should be at least 2.0 m. When attaching the weights to a wire, do not knot the wire, as this weakens it. It is better to twist the wire round itself, thus forming a loop from which to hang the weights.

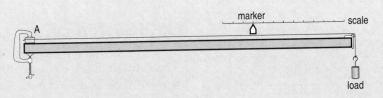

Fig 4.15 Tensile testing of wires.

Table 4.3 Materials for tensile testing

Material	Thickness/mm	Notes [a]
iron wire	0.2	
steel wire	0.08	44 SWG
copper wire	0.315	30 SWG
nylon monofilament	0.25	6 lb fishing line

[a] SWG = standard wire gauge

2. The marker should be about 50 cm from the pulley. Measure and record the original length from A to the marker with a small (2 N) load.

3. Note the original diameter, measured with a micrometer screw gauge.

4. Increase the load gradually in steps of 2 N. Record the increase in length. Note anything else that you notice as the wire or fibre stretches.

5. Measure its diameter when it has snapped. Examine the broken ends with a magnifying glass or microscope.

6. Plot graphs of load against extension.

7. Calculate the Young modulus (from the original slope) of the material.

INVESTIGATION

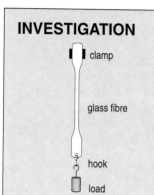

clamp

glass fibre

hook

load

Glass is a brittle material. It is difficult to measure its Young modulus, but you can investigate the stress needed to break a thin fibre of glass.

You can make a drawn-out glass fibre as follows: bend the end of a glass rod to form a hook to support the mass hanger. Soften the middle of the rod in a Bunsen flame, and draw it out into a short fibre. Suspend it as shown in Fig 4.16 and gradually load it until it snaps.

What other measurement must you make in order to find the stress that breaks the glass?

Fig 4.16 Tensile testing of glass fibre.

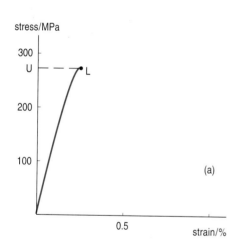

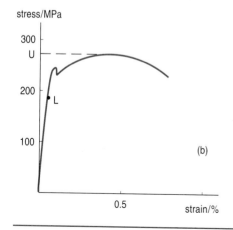

Interpreting graphs

In order to make the most of tensile testing experiments, we need to be able to interpret the stress–strain graphs that result. It helps to divide such a graph into two regions:

• up to point L, the elastic limit;

• beyond point L.

Elastic deformation

Fig 4.17 shows characteristic graphs for materials that show different behaviours under tension. In each case, the **elastic limit** (point L) is marked. (This is also known as the yield point.) If the material is stretched beyond this point, it will not return to its original length. (You may also be able to identify the limit of proportionality – the point at the top of the initial linear portion of the curve.)

For stresses below the elastic limit, the material undergoes **elastic deformation**; that is, if the stress is removed, it returns to its original length. The elastic energy stored as the material is stretched may be recovered as it is released.

We tend to think of stone as a very stiff material, but it does show elastic

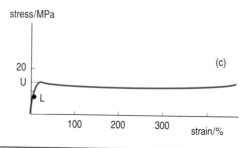

Fig 4.17 Stress–strain curves for **(a)** glass, **(b)** annealed low-carbon steel and **(c)** polyethene.

MEASURING MECHANICAL PROPERTIES

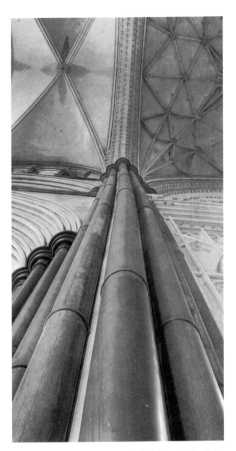

Fig 4.18 Bending in columns in Salisbury Cathedral.

deformation. Fig 4.18 shows how the columns that support the tower of Salisbury Cathedral are noticeably bent. This picture emphasises the way in which a long specimen of a material shows up the effects of applying a stress.

(*Note:* Hooke's law is usually taken to state that strain is proportional to stress, provided the elastic limit is not exceeded; in other words, the stress–strain graph is linear up to L. This implies that the elastic limit is the same as the limit of proportionality. In practice, this is not always the case. Stress–strain graphs are not perfectly linear. However, for many materials, Hooke's law is a useful approximation, and the Young modulus is a useful measure of stiffness.)

Plastic deformation

Beyond the elastic limit, the material undergoes **plastic deformation**. When the applied stress is removed, its shape has changed. Not all materials show plastic deformation – glass, for example (Fig 4.17(a)).

A material that undergoes considerable plastic deformation before breaking is said to be **ductile**. The ductility of a material may be expressed as the plastic strain it can undergo before breaking – you should have found that copper shows 20 or 30% ductility. Note that this is many times greater than the elastic strain – see Fig 4.17(b).

A material that undergoes little plastic deformation before breaking is said to be **brittle**; an obvious example is glass (Fig 4.17(a)), but many other materials also show this behaviour – cast iron is often brittle.

More properties

The **hardness** of a material is a measure of its resistance to plastic deformation under load. This is rather difficult to quantify; there are several tests that are in use, in which a piece of material is loaded using a standard indentor and a known force. The harder the material, the less it is indented.

The **toughness** of a material is a measure of its resistance to fracture. A lot of energy is required to break a tough material.

Finally, the **strength** of a material (or 'tensile strength') is the greatest tensile stress it can undergo before fracturing. This is indicated as point U (for 'ultimate') on the graphs of Fig 4.17. This is obviously an important consideration for engineers – a structure must be designed so that it does not experience as great a stress as this. In practice, a safety factor of 2 is usually allowed.

ASSIGNMENT

In the section above, we have defined several terms that are mechanical properties of materials: stiffness, strength, ductility, brittleness, hardness, toughness. These can be easily confused. Write short paragraphs to explain the differences between the following pairs of words:

1. elasticity and plasticity;

2. stiffness and strength;

3. ductility and brittleness;

4. hardness and toughness.

   Now, try to apply these terms to some everyday materials. Try stretching and bending some or all of the following: wooden and plastic cocktail sticks, paper, plasticine, bouncing putty, copper sheet, pottery, elastic, polythene. Which show elastic and plastic deformation? Which are brittle and which are ductile? Which are tough and which are hard? Which are stiff and which are strong?

MEASURING MECHANICAL PROPERTIES

4.6 The graph in Fig 4.19 shows the stress–strain graph for a polymer. Use the graph to determine:

(a) the Young modulus of the material;

(b) the tensile strength of the material.

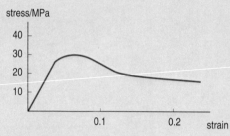

Fig 4.19 Stress–strain curve for the polymer ABS.

4.7 The stress–strain curves of a range of materials are shown in Fig 4.20. Which material:

(a) has the highest yield stress,

(b) has the greatest ductility,

(c) is the strongest,

(d) is the stiffest?

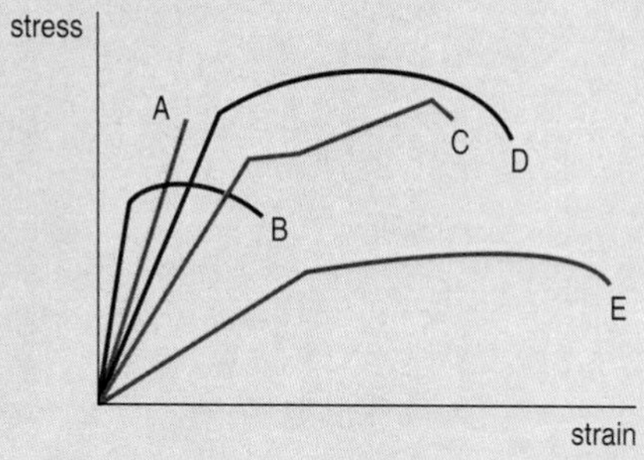

Fig 4.20 Stress–strain curves for five different materials.

4.8 Wood; glass; copper; a car tyre; plasticine; a biscuit; brick; a polyethene bag. Materials may be strong or weak; stiff or flexible; tough or brittle; elastic or plastic. Which of the above materials:

(a) are stiff,

(b) are brittle,

(c) are weak,

(d) are stiff *and* weak,

(e) show plastic deformation?

4.9 You are provided with several polymer threads of different degrees of stiffness and strength. You test them by stretching them by hand. Describe what you would expect to observe for a material that is:

(a) stiff but not strong;

(b) strong but not stiff;

(c) stiff and strong;

(d) neither stiff nor strong.

4.4 CREEP, FATIGUE AND HYSTERESIS

In many engineering applications – bridges, cranes, aircraft wings – materials are subjected to varying loads. Their mechanical behaviour cannot simply be investigated by a simple one-off tensile test. This is because the properties of a material often change with time – something that engineers must take into account in their use of materials.

Creep and recovery

You may have noticed, in the tensile testing investigation, that some of the wires and threads that you stretched showed a tendency to elongate gradually some time after the load was applied. This phenomenon is called creep, and would have important consequences in the design of, say, a suspension bridge. Nylon would be an unsuitable material for the supporting cables. What would happen to a fizzy lemonade bottle made from a plastic that showed considerable creep? Once the load is removed, the material will return towards its original dimensions. This is called **recovery**.

Creep becomes increasingly important at higher temperatures. For metals, creep begins at $(0.3–0.4) \times T_m$ (where T_m is the melting point in kelvins). For ceramics, creep begins at $(0.4–0.5) \times T_m$.

Polymers have no definite melting point; rather, they are hard and glassy below the glass transition temperature T_g (discussed below in Section 5.2). Well below T_g polymers show little creep – for example, perspex at room temperature.

QUESTION

4.10 Why are some car engine parts now made from ceramic materials rather than from metals? What disadvantage do ceramics have compared with metals?

INVESTIGATION

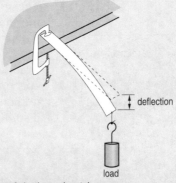

deflection

load

Fig 4.21 Determining the creep behaviour of plastics and metals.

Hazard warning
Take care to avoid cutting yourself on sharp metal edges.

Using the arrangement shown in Fig 4.21, you can look at the materials used for making lemonade containers to see how they respond to constant loading. You will need strips of metal and plastic cut from various containers, e.g. aluminium and steel drink cans, PET fizzy drink bottle, washing-up liquid bottle. Cut strips of metal and plastic approximately 20 mm wide. Ensure that they have cleanly cut edges.

Clamp each strip at one end so that you can apply a cantilever load. Tie a suitable weight onto the other end, or attach a piece of Blu-tak, so that the strip bends through about 30°. Record the deflection (in millimetres) produced initially, and then at intervals of, say, ½, 1, 2, 5, 10, 20, 30 min after loading.

Now try unloading the strips. Again, record the deflection at suitable intervals of time. The strip gradually returns towards its unloaded position.

Plot graphs to show how deflection varies with time. Can you see different behaviour for metals and polymers? Do all polymers behave in the same way? Which polymer is most suitable for a fizzy drink bottle, on the basis of this test?

Soft solder has a melting point of around 200 °C. It therefore demonstrates considerable creep at room temperature. Make a coil of about 20 to 30 turns of multicore solder by winding it around a rod of about 20 mm diameter. Secure the top end of the coil. Let the bottom end hang freely. Devise an arrangement to observe the creep, with time, of the coils under their own weight.

Fatigue

Many structures are subjected to vibrations in normal use. For example, the wings of an aircraft vibrate up and down as it flies; many parts of a car are subject to similar vibrations, and these can take their toll, causing the material to become weaker and sometimes deformed. The weakening and failure of materials as a result of repetitive, cyclical loading is called **fatigue**. Fatigue was the cause of a series of accidents involving Comet airliners in the 1950s.

Many polymers show little fatigue. You may be able to find everyday items where polymers are subjected to frequent flexing, as hinges or springs, for example. Children's lunch-boxes often have plastic hinges. Metals used in the same way would very soon break.

Fatigue failures have a standard pattern. With every cycle of loading and unloading, the material suffers some microstructural damage, which gradually accumulates until the damage leads to the initiation of a minute crack. The stress at the tip of the crack is much greater than anywhere else in the material, so the crack grows larger with every load cycle. Eventually the crack grows so much that the structure can no longer carry its load, and it breaks.

Fig 4.22 shows the result of a typical fatigue test on a specimen of steel. The specimen is subjected to a stress cycle of a certain value S, and the number of cycles N needed to break it is recorded. At high stresses, the specimen breaks after a relatively small number of cycles. The **fatigue limit** shows the maximum stress that the specimen can survive without suffering from fatigue, no matter how many stress cycles it is subjected to. For the specimen shown in Fig 4.22, the fatigue limit is reached after about a million cycles. This may take only a few hours to reach in an engine, and if it survives this long then it should be safe indefinitely.

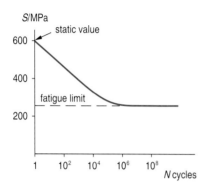

Fig 4.22 A typical S–N graph for steel. Notice that the fatigue limit is about half of the value of the tensile strength as measured in a static test.

QUESTION

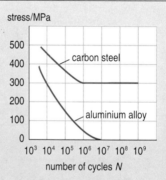

Fig 4.23 Fatigue test results for two alloys.

4.11 Fig 4.23 shows the results of fatigue tests on two different metals: a plain carbon steel, and an aluminium alloy.

(a) What is the fatigue limit for the steel?

(b) Explain why a component made from the aluminium alloy has a limited lifetime, whereas the same component made from the steel may have an unlimited lifetime.

INVESTIGATION

Investigate fatigue as follows:
Take strips of metal and plastic similar to those used in the creep experiment. Flex them back and forth by hand – you may be able to devise a mechanical means of doing this. If you bend them enough, and sufficiently frequently, they may become permanently deformed.

How does the behaviour of metal strips compare with that of plastic strips?

MEASURING MECHANICAL PROPERTIES

Hysteresis

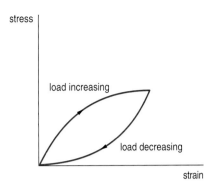

When a material is subjected to increasing and decreasing stress, it may show the phenomenon of **hysteresis**. This is represented in Fig 4.24. A sample of a material is gradually loaded, and then unloaded. From the graph, you will see that the extension (strain) is greater as the load is removed than when it was being added. The material remains partially strained as the load decreases.

The rubber of car tyres is subject to repeated compression and relaxation. Its response is represented by the hysteresis loop; each cycle of compression and relaxation is represented by one cycle around the loop.

The area under the stress–strain graph represents the energy stored in a stretched body. In a material that shows elastic hysteresis, energy is stored as the material is stretched or compressed, but less energy is released when the stress is removed. The area of the hysteresis loop represents the energy transferred to the material in each cycle.

You can observe this energy by repeatedly flexing a strip of plastic. After a while, it will become quite warm.

Fig 4.24 Hysteresis in the extension of rubber.

INVESTIGATION

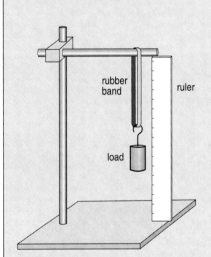

Fig 4.25 An arrangement for investigating hysteresis in a rubber band.

Investigate hysteresis as follows:

Hang a rubber band from a clamp – see Fig 4.25. Gradually load it in steps of 1 N or 2 N. Measure and record the length of the band each time. When the band is so loaded that it is becoming difficult to stretch further, gradually reduce the load back to zero, again recording the length.

Plot a single graph of load against extension. Use arrows to indicate increasing and decreasing load.

QUESTION

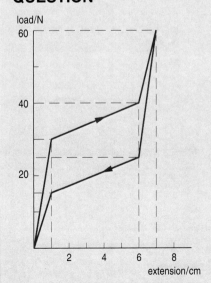

Fig 4.26

4.12 The graph in Fig 4.26 shows the load–extension graph for a hypothetical rubber band. Use the graph to estimate:

(a) the work done in stretching the band;

(b) the elastic PE released when the band is unloaded;

(c) the energy dissipated during this loading cycle.

4.5 CASE STUDY: DESIGNING A CANTILEVER

Fig 4.27 This bridge is designed to carry very heavy, varying loads.

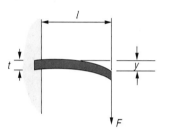

Fig 4.28 A cantilever bending under an applied load.

Introduction

Civil engineers require load-bearing beams such as box-section girders for bridges (Fig 4.27) and I-beams for supporting floors and roofs of buildings. Such beams, supported at one or more places along their length, will suffer deformation under load. The engineer must decide on the amount of deformation permissible for the expected load and select a material that has the desired characteristics.

In this case study we will see how to select a material from which to make a rectangular beam of minimum mass that will deform by a specified amount for a given load, and to evaluate the cost for alternative materials.

Identifying the relevant material properties

Let us consider the simplest case of a beam of square cross-section of side t, and length l, held rigidly at one end – see Fig 4.28. A maximum force F is applied at the free end to produce an elastic deflection y. We will assume that the weight of the beam is small compared with F.

A designer will wish to make a bridge with the lowest possible mass M for a given length l.

It can be shown that the deflection of such a beam is given by

$$y = 4l^3 F / E t^4 \tag{4.1}$$

where E is the Young modulus of the material.

We can also deduce a simple expression for the mass M of the beam in terms of its density ρ:

$$M = \rho l t^2 \tag{4.2}$$

Now we can eliminate t from these two equations, and deduce an expression for the mass of the beam:

$$M = \rho l (4l^3 F / y E)^{1/2}$$

This expression is easier to understand if we separate it into two terms:

$$M = (4l^5 F / y)^{1/2} (\rho^2 / E)^{1/2}$$

The first term depends on the design of the bridge; the second term depends on the material used. To minimise the mass of the cantilever, the designer must choose a material with a low value of $(\rho^2/E)^{1/2}$.

Table 4.4 Data for beam materials

Material	$(\rho^2/E)^{1/2} \times 10^3 / \mathrm{kg\,m^{-2}\,N^{-1/2}}$	Price, $P/\pounds\,\mathrm{kg^{-1}}$
steel	17	0.21
concrete	12	0.13
CFRP [a]	2.9	90
wood	5.5	0.20

[a] CFRP is the abbreviation for carbon-fibre-reinforced plastic

Table 4.4 gives data for several possible materials from which a beam might be made.

1. Which material has the best value of $(\rho^2/E)^{1/2}$?

2. Which is the next best alternative?

3. What advantage does this have over the first choice?

4. Why is it unlikely that the first-choice material would be used in a large-scale civil engineering structure?

MEASURING MECHANICAL PROPERTIES

5. Suggest reasons why wood is not used to make a chassis to support the weight of a vehicle.

From this analysis, you will see that wood has a low value of $(\rho^2/E)^{1/2}$; that is, it is relatively light for a given stiffness. This is why wood is so widely used in house building, and in sport for bats, racquets, frames and club shafts. CFRP would be too expensive for most large structures. Steel is much heavier for a given stiffness.

Calculating the cost

Suppose the engineer wishes to build a structure having the required mechanical properties, but as cheaply as possible. Table 4.4 shows the price per kilogram P for each of the materials. To minimise the cost, we need to find which material has the lowest value of $M \times P$; in other words, we need the lowest value of $(\rho^2/E)^{1/2} \times P$.

6. Calculate this quantity for each of the materials, and comment on the values you find.

Wood, concrete and steel are relatively cheap, and they are widely used in the construction industry. Clearly, carbon-fibre-reinforced plastic is too expensive for this purpose, but with improved production processes it may become cheaper in the future. It may be worth the extra cost to use it where lightness and stiffness requirements dominate cost, e.g. aircraft components and high-performance tennis racquets.

Wood appears to be a valuable material for constructing lightweight stiff structures, but it is not used to construct bicycle frames. Steel tube is generally used for this purpose. The analysis for tubular structures gives a different result from solid rectangular structures, and in this case steel is favoured over wood. Hence the absence of wooden bicycle frames!

In this case study, we have analysed a very simple situation in which only two criteria were considered. Many other factors have to be taken into account by practising engineers. These include: availability of materials; ease of transportation and handling; ease and cost of fabrication; effects of the environment upon the material. All of these influence the choice of material selected for a particular purpose.

SUMMARY

Several different properties must be measured in order to give a general description of the mechanical behaviour of a material. These properties include stiffness, strength, hardness and toughness. Some materials are ductile (they show plastic behaviour); others are brittle, and show only elastic behaviour.

Materials engineers need to take account of these properties, and many others, in their choice of materials to suit a particular design requirement.

Fig 4.29 summarises how stress and strain are related for a plastic material.

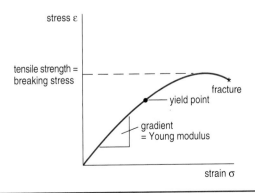

Fig 4.29 Summarising the stress–strain relationship for a plastic material.

Chapter 5

MECHANICAL PROPERTIES AND MICROSTRUCTURE

So far, we have only attempted to describe the phenomena that are important in our use of materials. We have developed a vocabulary for talking about what happens when loads are applied to materials; we hope you have also developed a feel for the meaning of these terms, by handling some materials.

Now we need to look at what is happening on the microscopic scale, to understand why different materials behave differently.

LEARNING OBJECTIVES

After studying this chapter you should be able to:

1. give simple explanations in terms of microstructure of the mechanisms of elastic and plastic deformation of metals, ceramics and polymers;

2. discuss the ways in which the mechanical properties of a polymer differ above and below the glass transition temperature T_g;

3. give simple descriptions of the mechanisms of brittle and ductile fracture;

4. give examples to illustrate how the microstructure of a material is modified to improve its mechanical properties.

5.1 STRETCHING AND BREAKING

Elastic deformation

When a small tensile stress is applied to a solid, it stretches slightly. We are pulling against the attractive forces between the particles of the solid. Providing there is no irreversible movement of particle past particle, the solid will return to its original length – see Fig 5.1. Since the force–separation curve is approximately a straight line near the equilibrium separation, it follows that the extension is proportional to the applied load. This is the origin of Hooke's law.

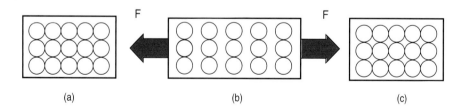

Fig 5.1 Elastic deformation under tensile load: **(a)** no load; **(b)** load applied; **(c)** load released. (*Note:* strain is greatly exaggerated.)

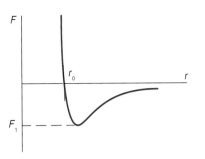

Fig 5.2 Force–separation curve for two particles.

Strength: a simple model

When a material breaks, its constituent particles separate. How can we relate this to the force–separation curve of Fig 5.2? When the solid is unstressed, the particles are separated by the equilibrium separation r_0. As the stress increases, their separation increases. If the force pulling the particles apart exceeds the value F_1 (the greatest attractive force between them), they will separate, and the solid is broken. Simple calculations show that the stress required is approximately one-tenth of the Young modulus; this stress is known as the **theoretical strength** of the material.

In practice, it is usually found that the breaking stress is less than 1% of E. In other words, the bulk material is much weaker than our simple model predicts.

It is important to realise that the strength of materials is generally found to be considerably less than predicted from a knowledge of interatomic forces – often hundreds or thousands of times less. If we can understand why this is so, we may be able to change the structure of the material, in an attempt to achieve a strength closer to the theoretical strength.

ASSIGNMENT

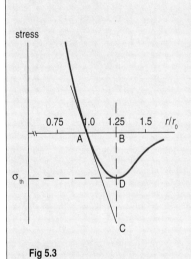

Fig 5.3

By studying the shape of the force–separation curve, you can see how the theoretical strength of a material is related to its Young modulus. Fig 5.3 shows the force–separation relationship for two adjacent atoms in a metal, expressed as a stress–strain graph.

Point D represents the point at which the two atoms separate, i.e. the metal breaks. The quantity σ_{th} is thus the theoretical strength of the material. Use the graph to answer the following questions.

1. What is the value of the strain at point D? By what percentage has the material stretched when it breaks?

2. How does this compare with the behaviour of a typical metal?

Now consider the triangle ABC. The line AC is a tangent to the curve at point A.

3. What is the significance of the gradient of this line?

4. D is approximately the midpoint of BC. From the graph, deduce the lengths of sides AB and BC.

5. Calculate the gradient of side AC, and hence show that the theoretical strength is approximately one-eighth of the Young modulus, i.e. $\sigma_{th} = E/8$.

ASSIGNMENT

Calculate the ratio (breaking stress)/(Young modulus) for each of the metals shown in Table 5.1. (Take care with units.) Comment on the results you obtain.

Table 5.1 Young modulus and breaking stress for some polycrystalline metals

Metal	Young modulus/GPa	Breaking stress/MPa
aluminium	70	6–40
copper	130	200–400
iron	210	200
lead	16	15
mild steel	210	250

Fig 5.4 Metals that undergo plastic deformation can be formed into useful shapes. (These are Royal Maundy coins.)

Plastic deformation

Many materials, including many metals and polymers, have a yield point beyond which they deform plastically long before they reach their theoretical strength. This behaviour is associated with the defects in their structure discussed in Chapter 2.

Metals

Most pure metals are characterised by their high **ductility**; this is a useful property, as it allows them to be drawn into wires and formed into other useful shapes – see Fig 5.4. The ductile behaviour of metals is an example of plastic deformation; it may be explained in terms of 'slip'.

(a)

(b)

(c)

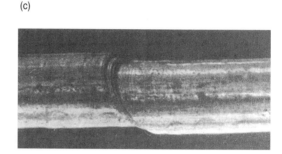

Fig 5.5 **(a)** Plastic deformation may occur in metals when planes of atoms slide over one another. **(b)** Such slip results in permanent extension. **(c)** The result of slip may be seen in the form of steps on the surface of a single crystal of cadmium.

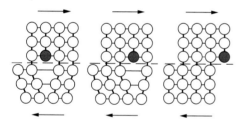

Fig 5.6 Movement of a dislocation, resulting in slip bands on opposite surfaces.

Slip occurs when planes of atoms slide over one another. In many metals, this takes place on the close-packed planes – see Fig 5.5(a). When a single crystal is deformed, the results of slip may be observed on the surface in the form of ledges or 'slip bands' – see Figs 5.5(b) and (c).

Slip occurs more readily when dislocations are present. If a dislocation moves through the crystal, the effect is of one crystal plane moving over another. The whole plane does not move simultaneously. This is often likened to moving a carpet across the floor by introducing a ruck – moving the ruck across the carpet results in the carpet moving across the floor – see Fig 5.6. This is much easier than moving the whole carpet at once. You may have been able to simulate the movement of dislocations in the bubble raft experiment.

This may give you some idea of how a metal may be strengthened. We want to stop crystal planes from sliding over one another, and prevent the movement of dislocations. One approach is to remove all defects. Single-crystal whiskers may be made with very few dislocations. They are found to be very strong, but their small size makes them of limited use.

Alternatively, we may add defects to the metal. Dislocations cannot move readily past grain boundaries, impurities, second phases and other dislocations. Thus metals may be strengthened by alloying, working, heat-treating and so on. When a metal is cold-worked, mechanical work is done on it, and more dislocations are introduced. These become entangled with one another, and can no longer move. Metals with small grain size have many grain boundaries, which prevent movement of dislocations. The smaller the grain size, the higher the stress at the yield point.

In the investigation that follows, you can look at the effects of some of these processes on the strength of steel.

The heat treatment of steels

The microstructure and physical properties of materials depend on their history – the treatment they have received during manufacture and processing. In this experiment, you will look at the effect of different heat treatments on the mechanical properties of steels.

You will need three 10 cm lengths of steel wire or strip (clock spring or piano wire will do). Alternatively, use long sewing needles.

Prepare the silver steel specimens in the following ways:

1. Heat one to bright red heat in a Bunsen flame (temperature 800 °C). Withdraw it very gradually to cool it as slowly as possible.

2. Heat another to bright red heat, and then cool it rapidly by plunging it in cold water. This process is called **quenching**.

3. Heat and quench the third in the same way. Now turn the Bunsen flame down so that it is burning less fiercely but is still blue, not yellow. Clamp your specimen just above the flame. (The temperature here is about 300 °C.) Leave the specimen in place for 5–10 min. This process is called **tempering**.

Now break each specimen by clamping in a vice and gradually bending it over until it fractures.

Note the different behaviour of the specimens. Look at the fractured surfaces with a hand lens or microscope. Note your observations.

Can you explain the changes in mechanical behaviour brought about by these heat treatments?

Hazard warning
Wear eye protection.

Ceramics

Ceramics may be as strong as the strongest metals. They show little or no plastic deformation, because slip is far more difficult than in a metal. The crystal structures of ceramics are often more complex than those of metals, and slip would require ions of like charge sliding past each other. The electrostatic repulsion between them prevents this.

5.1   Why are ceramic materials brittle?

5.2 STRUCTURE AND PROPERTIES OF POLYMERS

Polymers show a wide range of responses to stress, which depend on temperature, degree of crystallinity and degree of crosslinking.

Amorphous polymers

The mechanical behaviour of polymers that are unable to crystallise in the solid state shows a strong dependence on temperature. Most of these polymers at room temperature are either brittle glassy materials or they are rubbery. For each there is a characteristic temperature, called the **glass transition temperature**, T_g. Below T_g segments within the molecules are unable to move, the material is stiff, with a high Young modulus; it is often brittle and glass-like. Above T_g there is sufficient thermal energy to allow motion of segments of the chains, the Young modulus decreases and the material is rubbery. This behaviour of polymers such as perspex is exploited to fabricate shaped components such as crash-helmets – Fig 5.7 – from flat sheets in the process known as vacuum moulding.

(Non-polymeric amorphous materials do not show rubbery behaviour. They are liquid above T_g and glassy below T_g.)

Fig 5.7

The glass transition temperature
Perspex is a typical example of a glassy polymer. Its T_g is 120 °C. You can try an experiment to illustrate its behaviour around T_g. Take a strip of perspex 12 cm × 1.5 cm × 1 cm and put it in an oven at 140 °C for about 15 to 20 min.

Put on heat-resistant gloves and remove the strip from the oven. You should find that you can bend it or twist it easily and that it will recover provided that the strain is not too large.

Try putting a twist in the strip, then cooling it under the tap. Replace the strip in the oven and look at it again after about 15 min. It should have returned to its original shape; it has behaved elastically.

Viscoelasticity

As the temperature of a polymer increases from T_g towards the melting point, there is increasingly greater freedom of movement of segments. The molecular chains are able to slide past one another like molecules in a liquid. In this region the material is said to be **viscoelastic**. Its response to deformation is a combination of the elastic behaviour of a solid and the viscous behaviour of a liquid. The behaviour of viscoelastic materials is dependent on time as well as temperature. Bouncing putty is an interesting material that illustrates this.

ASSIGNMENT

Bouncing putty
Bouncing putty is a silicone-based polymer that has a T_g of −100 °C. If you pull it, you deform it irreversibly; it flows. It exhibits viscous liquid-like behaviour.

1. Why does the material show permanent deformation? Think about the movement of the molecular chains while the material is being stretched.

If you drop a ball of bouncing putty, you apply a stress for an instant at impact. It bounces; it behaves elastically.

2. If the material is not permanently deformed, what can be said about the positions of the chains before and after impact? What can you infer about the duration of the stress and the time taken for the chains to flow in this case?

Rubbers

From the example of bouncing putty, we see that the behaviour of the polymer depends on the time for which the stress is applied. Bouncing putty will even flow under the stress of its own weight. On a shorter timescale still, especially at low temperatures, bouncing putty becomes hard, brittle and glassy.

Rubbers are another group of amorphous polymers that show extraordinary behaviour. We are so familiar with these materials that we do not think of them as unusual. When natural rubber was first discovered, however, it was regarded as a great curiosity because of its low Young modulus and its ability to recover its original dimensions after being stretched from five to ten times its original length. You will recall that metals show a typical maximum elastic strain of 0.1% while that of other polymers is 1 to 10%.

The key to the understanding of the behaviour of rubbers lies in their molecular structure. The chains in rubber and other amorphous polymers are not straight. They consist of a large number of segments coiled randomly – Fig 5.8. If the material is deformed, the chains will uncoil to become less kinked. They may also slide past one another. This viscous slipping of the chains is prevented in rubbers by crosslinks between the chains. The molecules therefore return to their former or an equivalent state when the stress is removed. The coiled segments in rubbers act like springs, which recover their coiled state after being stretched.

Fig 5.8 Random coiled structure of a linear polymer.

Unusual temperature changes accompany changes in the extension of rubbers. Here is a simple experiment that you can try if you are not aware of these effects. Take a rubber band, at least 3 mm wide, touch it against your lip or forehead to sense its temperature. Stretch the rubber rapidly and sense its temperature again. Keep it stretched and allow it to come to thermal equilibrium. Now let it contract quickly, without letting go and again sense its temperature.

Let us try to explain these results. It will help if we think about the energy changes taking place in the rubber. When the rubber is extended, work is done. What happens to the potential and kinetic energy of the molecules during deformation?

When rubber is deformed, there is negligible change of volume. The molecules uncurl, but their average separation is unchanged; hence their potential energy is unchanged. The work done must therefore result in an increase in the kinetic energy of the molecules. According to kinetic theory, this is associated with an increase of temperature. Hence the rubber feels warmer. As the tension is relaxed, the rubber molecules curl up again. Work is done against the restraining forces at the expense of kinetic energy and the temperature falls.

Semicrystalline thermoplastics above T_g

We will take high-density polyethene as an example. We saw earlier that it has both amorphous and crystalline regions. It has a T_g of –120 °C. If the material is deformed, the two regions will respond differently. The crystalline regions behave in a similar way to an atomic crystal. Strain is produced in the covalent bonds by increasing the bond angles. In the amorphous region, segments of molecules will slide over neighbouring segments. Polyethene therefore shows viscoelastic behaviour and its deformation will depend on time and temperature.

It is found that if the material is deformed to a strain of 10% it will recover its original dimensions after a long period of time.

ASSIGNMENT

You can now try an experiment to see what happens when polyethene is stretched further. Cut a piece of polyethene from the rings that are usually used to hold together packs of canned drinks. Put two marks about 3 cm apart on the strip. Stretch it slowly with your hands until it is about four times its original length. Note any changes in the width and the appearance of the material during stretching. Unload and note how the length changes.

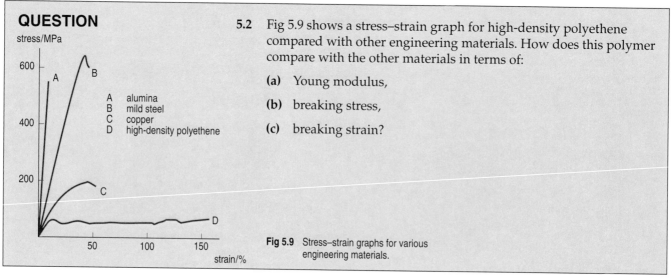

5.2 Fig 5.9 shows a stress–strain graph for high-density polyethene compared with other engineering materials. How does this polymer compare with the other materials in terms of:

(a) Young modulus,

(b) breaking stress,

(c) breaking strain?

A alumina
B mild steel
C copper
D high-density polyethene

Fig 5.9 Stress–strain graphs for various engineering materials.

Stress–strain behaviour

Fig 5.10 shows a typical stress–strain curve for a semicrystalline polymer under tension. Up to the point A the material shows a viscoelastic response – the strain is reversible. Between A and B the neck forms and plastic deformation sets in. The section within the neck, however, does not keep shrinking as it does with a metal. Instead, the width of the neck section remains constant and grows along the specimen in the direction of the tension. Eventually the material fractures at C without further necking. Considerable reorganisation of the molecular chains must be taking place during this process, which is known as **cold drawing**. Let us consider what is going on.

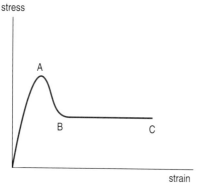

Fig 5.10 Typical stress–strain curve for a semicrystalline polymer.

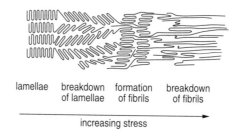

lamellae breakdown formation breakdown
          of lamellae of fibrils of fibrils

increasing stress

Fig 5.12 Effect of deformation on the crystal structure of a semicrystalline polymer.

Fig 5.11 Orientation of crystalline regions in a semicrystalline polymer:
(a) unstressed state; **(b)** under tensile stress.

Under small stresses the amorphous regions deform by the molecules sliding over one another. This causes the randomly oriented crystalline regions partially to align (Fig 5.11).

As the stress is increased, the packing of the lamellae breaks down and eventually they unfold and the molecules are rearranged to form fibrils – Fig 5.12. An increase of crystallinity accompanies this process and the polymer may become more opaque as the amount of amorphous material decreases. As the stress increases further, the fibrils break down – the polymer chains become unfolded to produce a highly ordered structure. At this stage the polymer is in the cold-drawn condition and its strength has increased considerably. This is because the load is now being taken by the covalent bonds of the chain atoms and not by the van der Waals bonds between the chains.

Cold-drawn polyethene tape is now being used to replace steel tape. It has the disadvantage, however, that its strength is anisotropic. It is weak in a direction at right angles to its length. If you try pulling your cold-drawn sample at right angles to the drawing direction, you will find that it is relatively easily split.

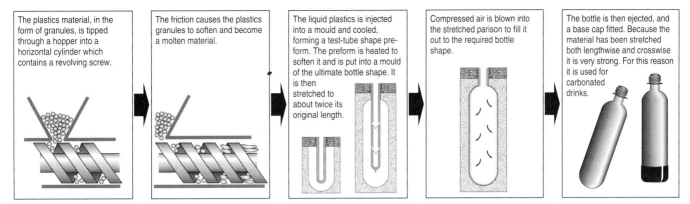

Fig 5.13 The fabrication of PET bottles for fizzy drinks. PET is poly(ethylene terephthalate) or terylene.

Polymers may be considerably strengthened by drawing them out in this way. Fig 5.13 illustrates the way in which a PET container for fizzy drinks is made. In the course of the manufacturing process, the material is stretched in two directions, making it considerably stronger and less likely to deform plastically when filled with a pressurised liquid.

QUESTIONS

5.3 Think about the anisotropic strength of drawn plastic tape. By considering the type of bonding **(a)** along the length of the tape and **(b)** perpendicular to the tape, account for this anisotropy.

5.4 Plastic drink cups are often very weak – they can be split vertically. The cup is formed by vacuum moulding, in which the material is stretched in one direction only. Explain why the PET bottle shown in Fig 5.13 is much stronger than one of these weak cups.

Thermosetting materials

These materials do not show plasticity, viscoelasticity or rubber-like behaviour. They have a high Young modulus and are brittle, rather like ceramics. They are generally strong.

QUESTION

5.5 Account for the properties of thermosetting polymers by considering the contributions made by:

(a) primary bonds,

(b) secondary bonds,

(c) crosslinking.

Consequences for fabrication

We have looked at the way in which materials show plastic deformation, and how this may be controlled. The processes used to limit plastic deformation result in materials that are stronger, harder and more brittle (less ductile). This makes them more difficult to form into a final shape. A balance must be achieved between ease of forming and strength of the final product.

The example above of the PET bottle (Fig 5.13) shows how a forming process may be devised in the course of which the material acquires the desired final strength. Copper piping, as used by plumbers, is drawn out (cold worked) to give a material of small grain size and high dislocation density, which is much harder and stronger than the parent material.

Creep

When a material is held under constant load for a period of time, creep may occur. Movement of crystallites may occur at grain boundaries, dislocations may move through the material, or diffusion of atoms and vacancies through the solid may occur. Diffusion is particularly important at temperatures near the melting point. You have already observed creep in the investigation in Section 4.4. It can be seen in everyday life in the sagging of lead pipes and the slow sliding of lead down church roofs (Fig 5.14).

Materials operating at high temperatures must be designed to be resistant to creep. For example, turbine blades in jet engines operate under great stress, as they spin in a very hot environment. Any gradual distortion due to creep could have disastrous consequences – see the case study later in Section 5.4.

The creep resistance of polymers can be increased by adding 'fillers' such as powdered ceramic to the polymer granules prior to moulding. Glass or silica may be used. The creep resistance increases roughly in proportion to the amount of filler added. Vinyl flooring, PTFE coatings on non-stick cooking utensils, and motor car bumpers, grilles and other plastic parts are often strengthened in this way. Composite materials made from polymers and fibres (e.g. GFRP and CFRP) show no creep coupled with high strength and low density.

Fig 5.14 Creep may be seen in lead roofing where ambient temperature is relatively high. The melting point of lead is 600 K.

QUESTION	5.6	How does the use of ceramic and plastic components in a motor vehicle help to improve its fuel efficiency?

5.3 FRACTURE

When a material breaks (fractures), the stress at points within it has become sufficiently great to separate the atoms of the material. There are different ways in which such high stresses may arise; in particular, we will look at the different ways in which ductile and brittle materials fracture.

Fracture and structure

The way in which a material breaks reflects its internal structure. If you try tearing a Kleenex tissue or a sheet of newspaper, you will find that it is easier in some directions than others. This reflects the arrangement of the wood fibres of which paper is made.

In stretching a copper wire, you will have observed the way in which a ductile material narrows down ('necking') before it breaks. The stress is increasing because the load is increasing and the cross-sectional area is decreasing. This region of greatest stress rapidly narrows until fracture occurs. The result is often described as a cup-and-cone fracture – see Fig 5.15.

It has been found that small pores or **voids** form in the region of the neck, often associated with impurities and grain boundaries. These contribute

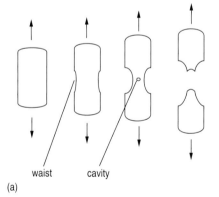

waist   cavity

(a)

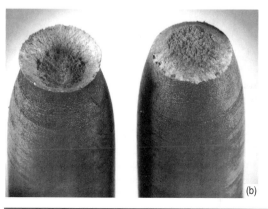

(b)

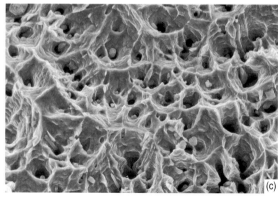

(c)

Fig 5.15 **(a, b)** Formation of cup-and-cone fracture surfaces. **(c)** Scanning electron micrograph of fracture surface.

MECHANICAL PROPERTIES AND MICROSTRUCTURE

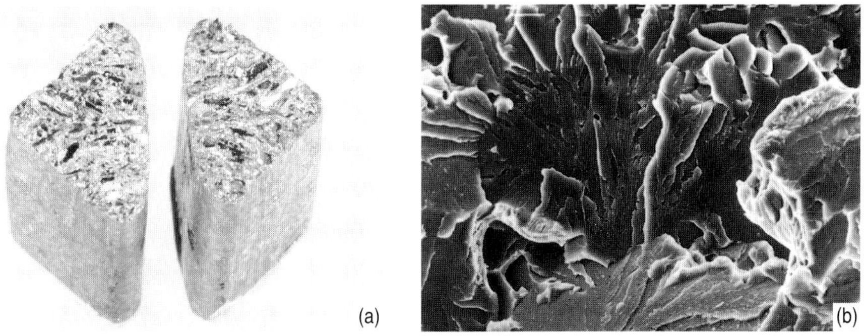

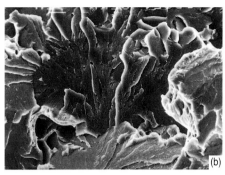

Fig 5.16 **(a)** Brittle fracture surfaces of zinc. **(b)** Scanning electron micrograph of fracture surface.

(a)

(b)

further to the reduction in cross-sectional area of the material, as they expand and coalesce to form internal cavities. The stress becomes very great, and the material breaks.

Brittle fracture

Ceramics, glassy materials and some metals break by a different mechanism, brittle fracture, associated with cracks and surface flaws. You have already seen the way in which a crack results in stress concentration, using photoelastic stress analysis in Chapter 4.

The result of brittle fracture of a bar of zinc is shown in Fig 5.16. There is no evidence of plastic deformation, unlike the cup-and-cone fracture surfaces in Fig 5.15.

INVESTIGATION

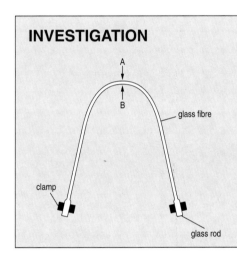

Another simple experiment is shown in Fig 5.17. A freshly drawn glass fibre is found to be very strong and can be bent without breaking. If its surface is scratched, it becomes much weaker.

Draw out a fine glass fibre. Stroke it gently at A, and bend it. Repeat with a new fibre scratched at B. Why does one fracture more readily than the other?

Fig 5.17 Fracture of a scratched glass fibre.

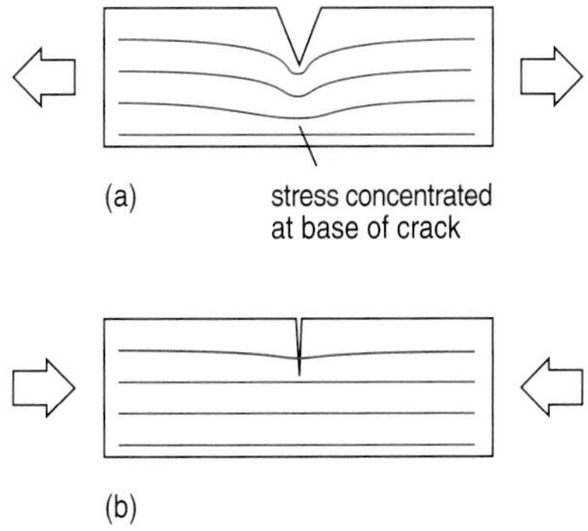

Fig 5.18 Stress lines in a cracked solid **(a)** in tension and **(b)** in compression.

Cracks are crucial in a region of material that is in tension – the stress tends to pull them open, and they can propagate through the material. In regions of compression, the stress tends to close the crack – see Fig 5.18.

Preventing brittle fracture

There are several ways in which crack propagation may be prevented. Many brittle crystalline materials do not crack as readily as glass, because the stress concentration at the tip of the crack results in plastic flow of the material. The material deforms so that the crack is blunted, the stress concentration is reduced, and the crack does not propagate.

Glass may be toughened in different ways. If the surface is in a state of compression, cracks will close up. This is used in making tough car windscreens. The screen is formed from hot glass, and then air jets are played on the surfaces to cause rapid cooling and contraction. Subsequently, the interior cools and contracts, pulling the outer layers into a state of compression. (You can often see markings on windscreens – these show the pattern of the air jets used.) If the screen actually breaks, the release of inner tension can be very dramatic.

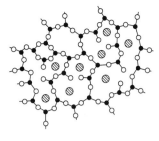

⊘ K ion

● Si atom

○ O atom

Fig 5.19 Potassium ions enter spaces in the Si–O structure of glass.

A similar effect is achieved by changing the chemical composition of the glass surface. Small ions, such as Na^+, are replaced by larger ones, such as K^+, by immersion in a molten potassium salt – see Fig 5.19. When the glass cools, the surface cannot readily contract, and is left in a state of compression.

These techniques have been used very successfully in practice, and many glass items such as jars and milk bottles can now be made much stronger and lighter than they were twenty or thirty years ago.

Composites

Some of the most successful man-made materials are composites, which have exceptional mechanical properties. They may be very stiff, strong or flexible, and resistant to plastic deformation and brittle fracture. You can investigate the behaviour of a simple composite material in the experiment that follows.

INVESTIGATION

Cut strips of newspaper to fit a plastic sandwich box or metal loaf tin. Lay them in the box or tin, soak them in water, and freeze overnight to form a solid block of ice strengthened with newspaper. Make a similar block of ice by freezing water in another similar box or tin.

Test your two frozen blocks to see how strong they are. You may need to use a hammer. Explain why one breaks more easily than the other. What role does the newspaper play?

ASSIGNMENT

1. Prestressed concrete makes use of the fact that the compressive strength of concrete is much greater than its tensile strength. Find out how this works.

2. Many composite materials such as fibreglass and carbon-fibre-reinforced plastic are made of stiff but brittle fibres in a plastic or resin matrix. Find out about the structure of these materials, and explain why they are strong and why they are not brittle.

3. Find examples of everyday materials that have been designed to minimise plastic deformation, and brittle and ductile fracture. There are some examples in the text, but you should be able to find others.

QUESTIONS

5.7 A strip of polyethene is stretched by applying a load, and then released. The load–extension graph is shown in Fig 5.20. Explain these observations:

(a) in macroscopic terms;

(b) in microscopic terms.

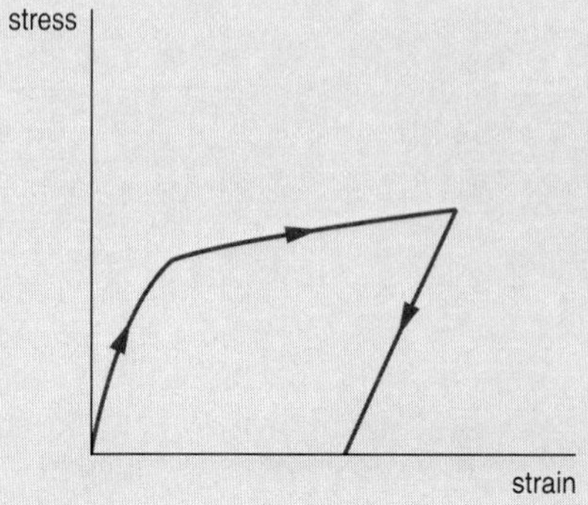

stress

strain

Fig 5.20 Stress–strain curve for the loading and unloading of polyethene.

5.8 Tungsten is used to make filaments for light bulbs. There are several reasons for this. Tungsten is a *ductile* metal. It shows little or no *creep* at high operating temperatures. Its microstructure is of long thin grains – see Fig 5.21 – making it *strong* and *flexible*. Thorium oxide and silicon dioxide are added to prevent *recrystallisation*.

Explain the terms in *italics*. Why is it desirable for tungsten to have these characteristics if it is to be used in filaments?

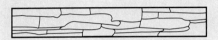

Fig 5.21 The microstructure of tungsten wire.

5.9 Explain what is meant by plastic deformation. Do all 'plastics' show this behaviour?

5.10 Diamond; copper; glass; steel; polyethene. Which of these materials has good stiffness and strength:

(a) because of the high density of covalent bonds;

(b) because the presence of foreign atoms prevents dislocation movement;

(c) because its amorphous structure prevents dislocation formation?

5.11 Explain the following observations of polymer behaviour in terms of microstructure and chain mobility:

(a) At temperatures below –70 °C natural rubber is a brittle solid, but at room temperature it may be strained by several hundred per cent without plastic deformation.

(b) Poly(chloroethene) (polyvinyl chloride, PVC) is a brittle solid at room temperature. At temperatures around 50 °C it can show elastic deformation of up to 5%. At still higher temperatures it shows an increasing tendency to suffer plastic deformation when strained.

In questions 5.12–5.14, which conclusions are correct?

5.12 Ductile fracture occurs:

(a) after considerable plastic flow;

(b) when dislocations are free to move;

(c) after a large number of cycles at a low level of stress.

5.13 When a metal is stressed repeatedly beyond its yield point, so that the dislocations become entangled with each other and are less free to move, it is likely to become:

(a) stronger;

(b) more ductile;

(c) more brittle.

5.14 Metals are often worked (forged, rolled, etc.) at high temperatures because:

(a) they are more ductile when hot;

(b) cracks form less easily;

(c) they become work-hardened.

CASE STUDY: MATERIALS FOR TURBINE BLADES

Background

Gas turbine engines are used in pumping stations along oil and gas pipelines, in electricity generation and for propulsion of vehicles ranging from warships to aircraft. They have a high power-to-weight ratio and are amongst the most efficient converters of fossil fuels into kinetic energy. They power our modern airliners.

In 1953 the first civil jet-propelled aircraft, the Comet, went into commercial operation, carrying about 50 passengers. Today's jumbo jets carry over 400 passengers. They may be powered by Rolls-Royce RB211 engines, which develop a thrust some ten times greater and generate twice the thrust per kilogram of fuel consumed compared with the Comet's engine.

In this case study we will see how the interplay of the development of materials, manufacturing processes and design has been the driving force behind the development of the gas turbine aero-engine.

Principles of propulsion

We need to have some understanding of how a gas turbine engine works before we can appreciate the properties required of the engine materials.

The power needed to propel all aerospace vehicles, from model aircraft to missiles, is supplied by accelerating a mass of gas. For planes the gas is air. The momentum imparted to the air by the engine provides the forward thrust. You are familiar with what happens when you release an inflated balloon and allow air to escape from it. It flies. A jet of air streams from the balloon, propelling it forward.

Aircraft engines develop propulsion in two ways. Propeller engines drive a large mass of air slowly; jet engines drive a small mass of air quickly. Large turbofan engines such as the RB211 combine both propulsive methods. Fan blades at the front of the engine act like propellers, while the core of the engine provides the jet propulsion.

A gas turbine engine consists of three main parts: the compressor, the combustion chamber and the turbine – Fig 5.22. Air is drawn into the compressor by the fan blades – the propellers – and compressed to about 30 times atmospheric pressure. Its temperature may rise to about 1000 K as a result. In the combustion chamber, fuel is injected into the heated air as a fine spray. Combustion raises the air temperature to its maximum value of about 1500 K with a further increase of pressure. The gas then passes into the turbine section where it is expanded at atmospheric pressure.

Turbine blades are forced to rotate by the hot gases moving over them – the same principle that is used in the windmill – to extract energy to drive the compressor. The gas then emerges through the nozzle to provide the thrust for propulsion.

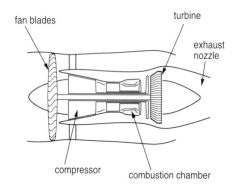

Fig 5.22 Section showing the components of the gas turbine engine.

The efficiency of heat engines

The thermal efficiency η of an engine is defined by:

$$\eta = (\text{useful work done in one cycle})/(\text{energy received from fuel})$$

For an ideal engine, η is related to the operating pressures and temperatures within the engine shown in Fig 5.23 by

$$\eta = 1 - T_4/T_3 = 1 - (1/r)^{0.29} \tag{5.1}$$

where r is the compression ratio P_3/P_4 of the turbine.

Real engines are less efficient than the ideal, but these equations nevertheless provide useful guidelines for establishing desirable operating conditions of temperature and pressure for real engines. The temperature T_3 and pressure P_3 at the entrance of the turbine section can be varied.

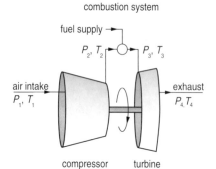

Fig 5.23 Diagrammatic representation of an operating gas turbine engine, showing temperatures and pressures at four stages.

MECHANICAL PROPERTIES AND MICROSTRUCTURE

1. Look at equation (5.1) and decide how the engine efficiency η changes with the temperature ratio T_4/T_3 and the compression ratio P_3/P_4. Assume that P_4 and T_4 are one atmosphere and 273 K respectively. Decide whether high or low values of P_3 and T_3 give greater efficiency.

The η value will become closer to 1 as both T_3 and P_3 increase. Engines thus become more efficient as turbine entry temperature T_3 and pressure P_3 rise. The actual operating conditions will be set by the limitations of the materials used in the engine.

The working conditions of the turbine blades

From equation (5.1) above, it follows that, for greatest efficiency, the hot gases from the combustion system should enter the turbine at high temperature and pressure.

Turbine blades rotate at a typical speed of 10 000 rpm for long periods in an environment of combustion products at a temperature of about 1500 K. They must withstand impact and erosion from debris drawn in with the air stream. In addition, different parts of the blade may be at different temperatures. They will be subjected to large and rapid temperature changes when the engine is started up and turned off.

2. Read carefully through the set of conditions listed in the previous paragraph. Think about the properties required of the material from which the blades are made. What can you say about each of the following properties?

   (a) creep resistance,

   (b) corrosion resistance,

   (c) toughness,

   (d) mechanical fatigue resistance,

   (e) density.

3. Why do you think that ceramics are not used at present for turbine blades? They have high melting points and therefore good creep resistance. They have good corrosion resistance and low density combined with high stiffness. All these would seem to make them suitable materials for turbine blades.

Turbine blade super-alloys

Turbine blades can be required to withstand a take-off stress of 250 MPa for 30 h at 850 °C with less than 0.1% irreversible creep strain. An alloy containing no less than eighteen constituents has been evolved to meet these demands. Its composition is shown in Table 5.2.

Table 5.2 Composition of creep-resistant turbine blade super-alloy

Element		Amount/wt%	Element		Amount/wt%
nickel	Ni	59	molybdenum	Mo	0.25
cobalt	Co	10	carbon	C	0.15
tungsten	W	10	silicon	Si	0.1
chromium	Cr	9	manganese	Mn	0.1
aluminium	Al	5.5	copper	Cu	0.05
tantalum	Ta	2.5	zirconium	Zr	0.05
titanium	Ti	1.5	boron	B	0.015
hafnium	Hf	1.5	sulphur	S	<0.008
iron	Fe	0.25	lead	Pb	<0.005

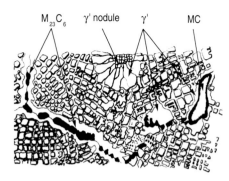

Your first question, when confronted with such a recipe, might be: 'Why so many elements and what does each do?' We will now try to answer this question in order to understand how the microstructure and the properties of the material depend on its composition.

Alloying elements help to minimise creep by reducing slip. Obstacles in the form of insoluble precipitates are introduced to hinder deformation. By far the most important of these obstacles are particles of the so-called γ' phase. A schematic representation of the microstructure of super-alloys is shown in Fig 5.24. Table 5.3 lists the functions of the different elements used.

Fig 5.24 Microstructure of a super-alloy showing γ' phase, matrix-strengthening carbide MC, and grain boundary-strengthening carbide $M_{23}C_6$.

Table 5.3 Functions of different elements used in super-alloys

Purpose	Cr	Al	Co	Mo	W	Ti	Ta	Nb	Hf	C	B	Zr
matrix strengtheners	✔		✔									
γ' formers		✔				✔	✔	✔				
carbide formers	✔			✔	✔	✔	✔	✔	✔			
oxide scale formers	✔	✔										
grain boundary strengtheners									✔	✔	✔	✔

We shall now try to see how this microstructure is responsible for the properties of the super-alloy. Its mechanical behaviour is the result of action taken to reduce the movement of dislocations through the material.

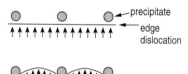

precipitate
edge dislocation

Fig 5.25 Effect of matrix strengtheners (precipitates) on dislocation movement.

- Any irregularity in the crystal will hinder the progress of a dislocation. Strains set up around substitutional atoms impede the movement of dislocations. As the temperature of a metal increases, creep becomes more pronounced. More vacancies appear as the temperature rises and diffusion of atoms becomes easier. Additives that make diffusion more difficult, therefore, enhance **creep resistance**.

- Hard precipitates are more resistant to deformation. Their presence in a softer matrix makes it more difficult for planes of atoms to slip over one another. We can think of them as acting like boulders thrown into a stream to dam the flow of water. It is also difficult for dislocations to pass through regions with closely spaced hard precipitates. A dislocation passing through such a region has been compared with trying to blow up a balloon in a bird cage. It is difficult for the balloon membrane to pass through the bars – Fig 5.25. The dislocation is similarly confined by the precipitates.

- The grain boundaries become the source of weakness following the strengthening of the matrix. If they are filled with hard materials, which are firmly bonded to the grains, it becomes more difficult to shear the grains apart. Grain boundary strengtheners act rather like the cement in crazy paving.

We will now look at how each element contributes to this complex structure.

Nickel crystallises in a ccp structure. **Cobalt, tungsten** and **chromium** dissolve in the nickel, forming a solid solution known as the γ phase. This makes up the bulk of the alloy. The alloying atoms may be different in size from nickel atoms and they are distributed randomly throughout the nickel matrix. Strains are generated around the foreign atoms in the matrix because of their disparity of size. This strengthens the nickel matrix.

Aluminium and **titanium** form stable compounds such as Ni_3Al and Ni_3Ti. Some of the aluminium atoms may be replaced by **tantalum**. These

MECHANICAL PROPERTIES AND MICROSTRUCTURE

compounds constitute a separate phase – the γ' phase – which has a similar packing arrangement and spacing as the γ matrix. Furthermore, the particles of the γ' phase have the same crystal orientation as the neighbouring γ phase, and do not disrupt its regularity. However, because these particles are extremely hard, they are very resistant to shear deformation.

Molybdenum and **tungsten** make it more difficult for atoms to diffuse within the crystal. This enhances the high-temperature stability of the alloy, improving its creep resistance. **Molybdenum**, **tantalum**, **tungsten** and **titanium** form carbides (MoC, TaC, WC and TiC), shown schematically as MC on Fig 5.24. These also are very hard materials that act as obstructions to matrix deformation. Other carbides that have the general formula $M_{23}C_6$ accumulate at the grain boundaries, as can be clearly seen. The metal M in this case is usually **chromium**, but this carbide may often be quite complex and contain other metals such as Mo, Ni, Co or Fe. **Carbon**, **boron**, **zirconium** and **hafnium** also accumulate at grain boundaries. It is believed that they strengthen these regions by reducing the formation of cracks that lead to failure.

We have seen that one element may have a number of functions in strengthening the alloy. **Chromium** is a particularly good example. In addition to the two already mentioned, chromium forms a layer of oxide Cr_2O_3 on the blade surface. This greatly improves corrosion resistance.

Processing developments

Turbine blades were shaped by forging before the introduction of superalloys. But the new materials were so hard that they could not be forged or easily shaped by existing machining techniques; they had to be cast. A mould that is used only once is made for each blade. This makes the process of production more expensive.

Cast blades have a fine grain structure – Fig 5.26. The weakest parts of the structure are still the grain boundaries. As blade operating temperatures were pushed higher, this weakness became more important. Creep damage occurs in the direction of stress, along the axis of the blade. Grain boundaries perpendicular to the blade axis rupture – Fig 5.27. If these grain weaknesses could be eliminated, either by aligning the grains parallel to the stress axis, or by eliminating grains altogether, blade life could be increased.

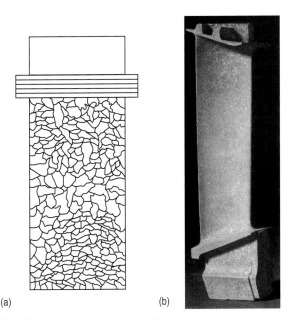

(a)　　　　(b)

Fig 5.26 Conventional as-cast turbine blade, showing grain structure.

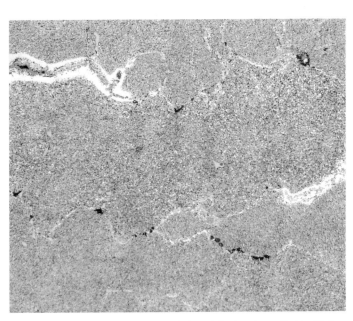

Fig 5.27 Cavity formation at transverse grain boundaries in a stressed turbine blade.

MECHANICAL PROPERTIES AND MICROSTRUCTURE

Grain boundaries perpendicular to the blade axis can be eliminated by directional solidification (DS). A mould of molten metal is enclosed in a hot zone of a furnace, and heat is removed from the bottom of the mould, allowing nucleation to occur. As the mould is gradually removed from the furnace, columnar grains develop along the axis (only) of the blade – Fig 5.28. The improved creep properties of DS blades allow the engine temperature to be increased by another 50 K, with further improvement in efficiency.

Complete elimination of grain boundaries has further advantages. A blade without grain boundaries is a single crystal. If the crystal can be grown in such a way that the blade axis is parallel to the face of the unit cell shown in Fig 5.29, further advantages accrue. Creep resistance is improved and the Young modulus is lower, reducing thermal stresses caused by temperature gradients across the blade.

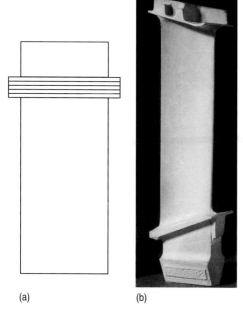

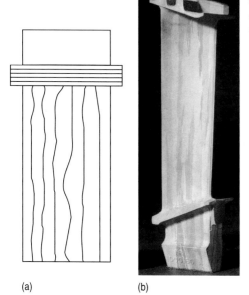

(a)   (b)

Fig 5.28 Directionally solidified grain structure.

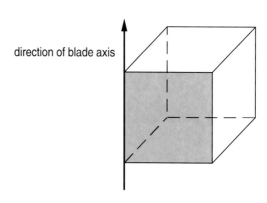

direction of blade axis

Fig 5.29 For directional solidification, best results are obtained with the blade axis along the crystal cube axis.

In addition, grain boundary strengtheners (carbon, boron, zirconium and hafnium) are not needed. All these elements contribute to lowering of the melting point. Their removal permits heat treatments to be executed to allow a more uniform distribution of the γ' phase. Furthermore, since hafnium costs £100 000 per tonne and is extremely scarce, a reduction of cost becomes possible.

Single-crystal blades are grown by incorporating a geometrical constriction into the mould or by the use of a seed crystal to initiate growth – Fig 5.30.

Design developments

Up to 1960 turbine blades operated at the temperature of the turbine inlet gases. The melting point of the alloys therefore set the upper limit for the engine operating temperature. If the blades could be cooled, they would be at a lower temperature than the driving gas and further advantages would be gained.

How can this be achieved? The internal combustion engine in the motor car is cooled by circulating a water-based fluid around the combustion cylinders. Water cooling of turbine blades is obviously difficult. Is there another fluid that can be used? In practice, air is used. An air-cooled blade is cast from a mould with a ceramic core. Chemical treatment after casting dissolves the core to leave a hollow blade. Air can be pumped through the blades to remove heat and reduce their temperature.

In the earliest air-cooled blades, air from the compressor was fed through ports passing along the core of the blade. This modification allowed inlet temperatures to be increased by 100 K without any modification of the alloy. Film cooling was developed next. Air is ejected through small holes over the surface of the blade. A cool boundary layer of air insulates the

(a)   (b)

Fig 5.30 Arrangement for production of single-crystal blade castings. A spiral constriction is used to produce the required crystal plane orientation.

MECHANICAL PROPERTIES AND MICROSTRUCTURE

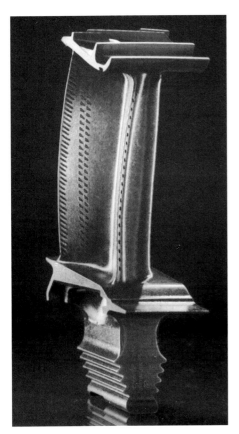

Fig 5.31 Air-cooling ports in a turbine blade.

surface of the blade from the hot gases – Fig 5.31. With this modification, the inlet gas temperature can be pushed above the melting point of the alloy. However, there is a limit to the amount of air that can be ducted through the blades. Thermal efficiency begins to fall because of the energy required to heat the ducted air.

The future

We have seen that the thermal efficiency of heat engines increases as the temperature of the ignited fuel–air mixture increases. Metallurgists have systematically developed improved alloys that allowed this temperature to be pushed progressively higher. However, improvements in thermal efficiency resulting from alloy development and blade cooling are approaching a limit. Further advances can best be made by developing new methods of propulsion and new materials.

There is now world-wide interest in developing ceramic materials for use in high-temperature engines. Ceramics are resistant to oxidation and their high melting point confers greater creep resistance at high temperature. These two properties would allow all-ceramic engines to run at high temperatures with improved thermodynamic efficiency. Such engines of both turbine and reciprocating design have been built and run. However, there are a number of problems to be solved before they can be mass-produced for the automotive industry with the degree of reliability of all-metal engines.

At present ceramics are being used in engines to coat metal parts to provide a thermal barrier, and to make individual non-moving parts in the combustion zone and wear-resistant components such as valve seats. They are being increasingly used in car and truck engines, but it may be many years before we are driving vehicles with all-ceramic engines.

SUMMARY

The mechanical properties of materials can be explained in terms of their microstructure. Many materials are found to be weaker than would be expected from a consideration of the forces between the particles of which they are made. This is because of defects in their structures. By controlling microstructure, improved mechanical properties can be achieved.

EXAMINATION QUESTIONS: Theme 2

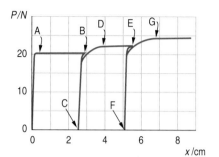

T2.1

(a) The graph shows the variation of extension, x, with tensile force, P, for a copper wire of initial length 120 cm as P is increased and then decreased repeatedly. From B and from E the extending force was gradually reduced to zero and then, from C and F respectively, increased again.

Describe, in *macroscopic* terms, the main features of the graph from C to G as the force changes.

Estimate the work done by the stretching force from C to F.

(b) The enamel of a human tooth is the hardest tissue in the body. It is a typical ceramic with a high compressive strength, a low tensile strength, a relatively high Young modulus and it is brittle. Dentine is the main structural material in the tooth. It is a composite material of much lower Young modulus than enamel and is relatively flexible and tough.

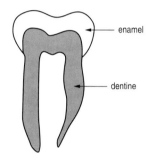

What is meant by the following terms used in the paragraph above:

(i)   a ceramic material,

(ii) a composite material,

(iii) a tough material?

Using the information given above, sketch, on a single set of axes, stress–strain graphs for enamel and for dentine. Give both positive strains (tension) and negative strains (compression) on your graphs.

(ULEAC 1993)

T2.2

When the surface of a glass fibre is roughened its tensile strength decreases.

Explain this observation by referring to the structure of a glass giving clear diagrams to support your explanation.

(WJEC 1992)

T2.3

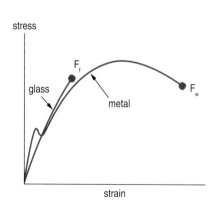

(a) Draw a diagram representing a dislocation in the lattice of a single crystal free of any other defects. Show how the motion of such dislocations may result in the plastic deformation of a single crystal under stress.

(b) The graph shows how the tensile stress varies with the tensile strain for a metal wire and a glass fibre. The points at which the wire and fibre break are labelled F_w and F_f respectively.

(i)   By making reference to the corresponding graphs, outline the mechanisms leading to the breaking of the wire and the fibre as the tensile stress increases from zero.

(ii) Redraw the graphs. For each of the specimens show the change you would expect in the *form* of the graphs had the applied stress been gradually reduced to zero after reaching about 80 per cent of the corresponding maximum possible value.

(c) Steel used in the manufacture of springs must not suffer a permanent set during use; that is, it must spring back. Discuss the ways in which this property can be achieved in the production of spring steel.

(NEAB 1990)

T2.4

The graphs show stress–strain curves for samples of wood (parallel to the grain), glass and aluminium, respectively.

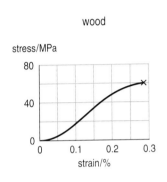

wood

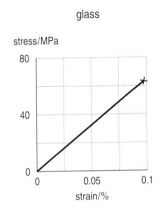

glass

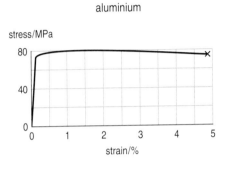

aluminium

(a) (i) Describe briefly the structure of aluminium. Account for the shape of its stress–strain curve up to and including its fracture point which is indicated as X on the graph.

(ii) The Young modulus of aluminium is 7.0×10^{10} Pa. Obtain a value for the Young modulus of each of the other materials.

(b) Engineers frequently wish to design rigid, yet light, structures. One measure of rigidity-to-weight is the numerical value of the quantity (Young modulus)$^{1/2}$/(density).

(i) Quote one application where rigidity and lightness are both required.

(ii) Using your answers to part (a) (ii) together with the data given below, place the materials wood, aluminium and glass in descending order of rigidity-to-weight.

(iii) Describe other properties of these materials which cause engineers to select aluminium in preference to the other two, even when low rigidity-to-weight is required.

(Density of wood = 600 kg m^{-3}, density of aluminium = 2700 kg m^{-3}, density of glass = 2500 kg m^{-3}.)

(ULEAC 1989)

T2.5

(a) (i) Explain why X-rays and not light are used to investigate the microstructure of materials.

(ii) Discuss in terms of microstructure the appearance of both sharp and diffuse rings in the X-ray diffraction pattern typical of high density polythene.

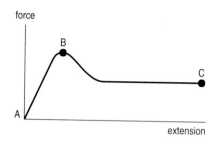

force

B

C

A

extension

(b) The figure shows a typical force–extension graph for a strip of high density polythene under tension.

The material shows a *viscoelastic* response between A and B with the onset of necking occurring at B. Necking continues until the material fractures at C.

(i) State what is meant by the term *viscoelastic* and explain the phenomenon in terms of the microstructure of polythene.

(ii) What changes in the microstructure are responsible for the formation of a *neck* in the specimen under tension?

(iii) State how the strength of the material will vary with direction in the region of the neck. Outline the reason for the observed variation in strength.

(iv) Sketch the X-ray diffraction pattern you would expect for the necked region. Indicate the direction of applied stress.

(c) High density polythene is an example of a *thermoplastic* whereas melamine is an example of a *thermosetting* plastic.

(i) State what is meant by each of the terms *thermoplastic* and *thermosetting*.

(ii) State *one* product for *each* type of material, naming the plastic used and giving a reason why the material is suited to the chosen product.

(NEAB 1992)

Theme 3

OPTICAL, ELECTRICAL AND MAGNETIC PROPERTIES

Although the mechanical properties of materials are of vital significance in many applications, materials have a great range of other properties that make them more or less useful in different applications.

Window glass, copper wiring, porcelain insulators, ferrite magnets, photochromic spectacles, light-emitting diodes, solid-state lasers – all these depend on materials with particular physical properties. The properties that matter in these applications may be optical, electrical, magnetic or thermal.

All these applications depend on materials that have been chosen and developed by materials engineers. They have been designed. Semiconductors are a class of materials that have been designed to have specific electrical and optical properties. They are used in many different applications and devices – you probably own several. Semiconductor engineering has had a considerable impact on our lives.

In Theme 3 we will look at the optical, electrical and magnetic properties of materials, and see some of the ways in which the microstructure of materials may be designed to give the properties we require.

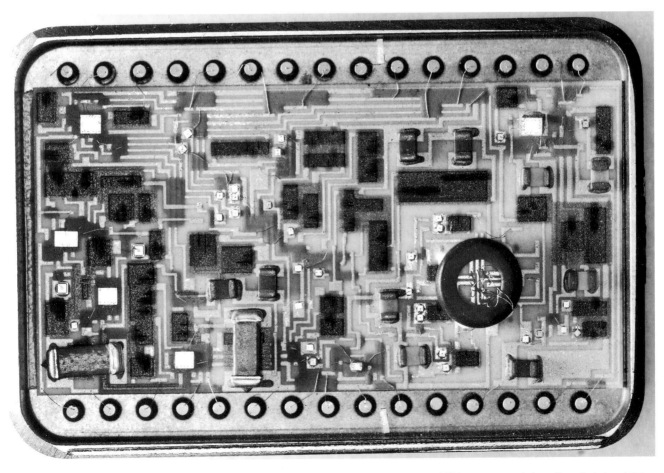

This thick-film hybrid microcircuit measures approximately 4 cm × 2 cm. Many different electronic components are laid down on a ceramic base. These include resistors, multilayer capacitors, a ring-shaped ferrite inductor and silicon integrated circuits; the materials for these components include metals, ceramics and polymers.

Chapter 6

OPTICAL PROPERTIES

The optical properties of a material determine how it interacts with light. We might be choosing glass for a lens or for an optical fibre, or metal for an item of jewellery, or a plastic film for improved double glazing. In all of these cases, it is how the material absorbs, transmits or reflects light that determines the best material for the job.

LEARNING OBJECTIVES

After studying this chapter you should be able to:

1. explain the origins of absorption spectra of solids in terms of changes in electron energies;

2. describe the differences in energy band structure between insulators, metals and semiconductors.

6.1 OPTICAL ABSORPTION AND EMISSION

Introduction

In order to appreciate the importance of materials with particular optical properties, we will start by considering an everyday material – window glass. Try to answer questions 6.1–6.3 now.

QUESTIONS

6.1 What optical and mechanical properties do we require of a material used for windows?

6.2 If you look at a sheet of glass edge-on, or a glass block or rod, what do you observe? Is it perfectly transparent and colourless?

6.3 You may have noticed that glass in the windows of old buildings is often difficult to see through. What defects result in this poor quality?

Glass has been used as a material for windows for over two thousand years. At first, it was difficult to fabricate even small sheets of glass, and so windows were small and expensive. Nowadays, glass is mass-produced and readily available as large, flat sheets.

Obviously, glass is selected for its transparency to visible light. It must also be stiff and reasonably strong. It must not react with air or rain water, and it must be cheap and easy to manufacture in flat sheets. You will have noticed that, if you look through a glass sheet or block edgeways, it is coloured – perhaps bluish green. The greater the thickness of glass through which you are looking, the stronger the coloration. Some frequencies of light are being absorbed by the glass.

Old glass may be of poor quality because of impurities, bubbles, surface cracks and flaws, inhomogeneities of composition, regions where devitrification has occurred, ripples and other non-uniformities. All of these contribute to the scattering or absorption of light.

The availability of this cheap transparent material is important. Think of the effect on our lives if glass absorbed light – or if the bricks we build our homes from were transparent!

In the technique of fibre optic communications, telephone messages are transmitted using light rays along glass fibres, which may be many kilometres in length. Clearly, window glass is not suitable. The light emitted by the transmitter would be absorbed by the glass long before it reached the receiver.

Impurities in the glass are the cause of this optical absorption. Fibre optic cables are made of high-purity glass. You can read more about fibre optics in the case study at the end of this chapter. To find out more about the way in which matter absorbs light, try the investigation.

INVESTIGATION

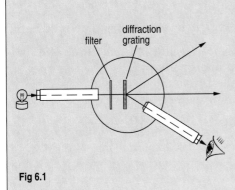

Fig 6.1

Absorption and emission spectra
The spectrum of light absorbed or emitted by a gas, liquid or solid can give us useful information about the energy states of electrons in the material. You can observe spectra using a spectrometer – Fig 6.1. (Hand-held spectroscopes are very useful for giving a quick impression of a spectrum.)

1. Set up a spectrometer with a diffraction grating. Use it to observe the spectrum of light from a sodium or mercury vapour lamp. You should see a line emission spectrum – a series of coloured lines. The light emitted by the lamp has been been split into its constituent wavelengths.

2. A line absorption spectrum is more difficult to observe. White light is shone through a gas or vapour. A white-light spectrum (red to violet) is observed, with dark absorption lines. Some wavelengths have been absorbed by the gas.

3. To observe absorption spectra, use a white light source. Observe its spectrum. (This is a continuous emission spectrum.) Now, place a straight-sided cell containing potassium permanganate solution in the path of the light from the collimator. Observe the spectrum. A range of wavelengths has been absorbed, giving a continuous absorption spectrum.

4. Repeat 3, using coloured filters and glass in place of the potassium permanganate solution. For each absorption spectrum, estimate the longest and shortest wavelengths of light present in the spectrum.

Explaining spectra

Gases are found to give line spectra. Only certain wavelengths are present in a **line emission spectrum** – see Fig 6.2; in a **line absorption spectrum**, certain wavelengths are missing, because they have been absorbed.

Solids and liquids generally give **continuous spectra**. Continuous ranges of wavelengths are present in the spectrum. The most familiar continuous spectrum is that of white light.

These two types of spectra arise because of the different arrangements of particles in the different states of matter. The atoms or molecules that make up a gas are described as *isolated* – that is, they are generally not in contact with their nearest neighbours, unlike the particles that make up a solid or a liquid.

Fig 6.2 The line emission spectrum for helium.

Absorption by isolated atoms

You have probably already studied the way in which isolated atoms absorb and emit light. Here is a brief recap:

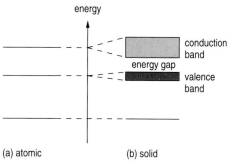

energy

conduction band

energy gap

valence band

(a) atomic   (b) solid

Fig 6.3 Energy levels of an electron.

1. When light interacts with matter, the light behaves as photons. The energy E of a photon is related to the frequency f of the light by the relation $E = hf$, where h is Planck's constant ($h \approx 6.6 \times 10^{-34}$ J s).

2. The electrons of an isolated atom can have only certain fixed values of energy. Intermediate values of energy are not possible. The possible energy values for an electron in a hypothetical atom are shown in Fig 6.3(a), in the form of a 'ladder' of increasing energy levels.

3. For an electron to gain energy, it must absorb a single photon of exactly the right energy, so that its new energy is one of the allowed values. The photon energy is equal to the change in the electron's energy between its initial and final states. A photon with slightly less or slightly more energy will not be absorbed. This is the origin of the line absorption spectrum.

4. An electron may lose energy by transferring to a vacant lower energy state. It emits a single photon whose energy is equal to the change of energy of the electron. This is the origin of the line emission spectrum.

Thus the absorption (and emission) of light by isolated atoms is associated with very well defined energy changes of the electrons. In particular, the electrons that are furthest from the nucleus (and least tightly bound) can most readily change their energy by absorbing or emitting photons of precise frequencies, giving rise to a line spectrum.

How can we account for the absorption spectra that you have observed in the investigation? We have discussed, in Chapter 1, the ways in which atoms join together to form solids. The outer electrons are involved – their energies are changed. What consequences does this have for the absorption of light by solids?

6.2 BAND THEORY

We can get a clue to the answer to this question by thinking about line spectra. Isolated atoms absorb or emit photons of a few narrowly defined values of energy, because their electrons can have only a few narrowly defined values of energy. Many solid materials show broad, continuous spectra – they absorb or emit photons of a range of values of energy, because their electrons can have a range of values of energy.

In a solid material, the outer electrons of neighbouring atoms interact – this is the origin of bonding. The result is that they can have a range of allowed values of energy. We say that they occupy a **band** of allowed energies, rather than narrow energy levels. Fig 6.3(b) shows the energy bands of a hypothetical solid.

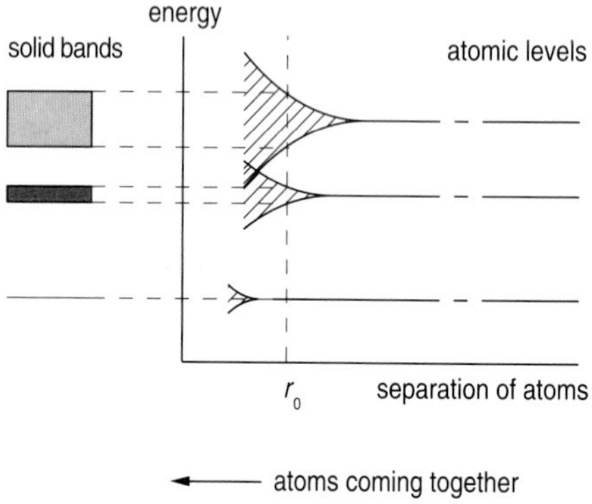

Fig 6.4 shows the way in which the energy levels of an atom are affected as atoms come together to form a solid. The outermost, most energetic, electrons are affected first; the narrow atomic levels are broadened to form ranges of allowed energy, or bands. The most energetic of these bands is called the **conduction band**. Electrons in this band are free to move throughout the solid. Below this is the **valence band**. Electrons in this band are unable to move through the solid.

energy

solid bands   atomic levels

r_0 separation of atoms

atoms coming together

Fig 6.4 As atoms are brought closer together to form a solid, their electronic energy levels overlap and broaden to form energy bands.

Between these two bands is an energy gap. An electron cannot have a value of energy that lies in this range; it is sometimes referred to as a **forbidden gap**. It corresponds to the forbidden gap between atomic energy levels.

Filling the bands

The electron energy levels of an atom can only accommodate a certain number of electrons. Similarly, the electrons in a solid cannot all be in the lowest energy state or band. In different materials, the bands are filled to different extents. This is illustrated in Fig 6.5.

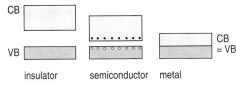

CB | VB
insulator | semiconductor | metal

Fig 6.5 Energy bands of electrons in solids: VB = valence band; CB = conduction band. In a metal, these two bands are the same.

In an **insulator**, the valence band is full and the conduction band is empty. There is a wide energy gap between the two bands. This is a reflection of the fact that, in ionic or covalently bonded materials, the electrons are held tightly to the ions or molecules.

In a **metal**, the outermost electrons give rise to the metallic bonding. They are free to move throughout the solid; they are the conduction electrons that are involved in the flow of electric current through the metal. In other words, there is no gap between the valence and conduction bands; there is a single band, which is partially filled.

A **semiconductor** is similar to an insulator. The valence band is full, and the conduction band is empty at absolute zero. However, at higher temperatures and if the energy gap is narrow, some electrons may have enough energy to enter the conduction band. The material will conduct, but not as well as a metal.

Optical absorption

How does this description of the allowed energy bands for electrons in a solid account for the observed band spectra of solids? And how does it explain why metals are opaque?

Let us think first about an insulator. The energy band picture of optical absorption is shown in Fig 6.6(a).

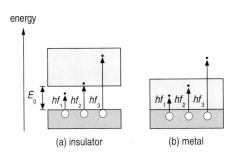

Fig 6.6 Optical absorption. **(a)** Photon hf_1 has insufficient energy to be absorbed. **(b)** Photon hf_3 has too much energy to be absorbed.

When a photon is absorbed, an electron is able to enter a higher energy state. This higher state must be vacant. The vacant states are in the conduction band; the electrons are in the valence band. Thus only a photon whose energy is at least as great as E_g (the width of the energy gap) will be absorbed.

In Fig 6.6(a), the photon represented by hf_1 has insufficient energy, and will not be absorbed. The photon hf_2 has just enough energy to allow an electron from the top of the valence band to reach the bottom of the conduction band. This photon is the lowest-energy photon that will be absorbed. Similarly, hf_3 will be absorbed.

WORKED EXAMPLE

Consider an insulator with energy gap 2.3 eV ($1\,\text{eV} = 1.6 \times 10^{-19}\,\text{J}$). Calculate the minimum frequency of light that can be absorbed by this material. Where does this frequency come in the spectrum?

Solution

Photon energy corresponding to the energy gap is

$$E = 2.3\,\text{eV} = 2.3 \times 1.6 \times 10^{-19}\,\text{J} = 3.68 \times 10^{-19}\,\text{J}$$

So the minimum frequency is

$$f = E/h = (3.68 \times 10^{-19}\,\text{J})/(6.63 \times 10^{-34}\,\text{J s})$$
$$= 5.55 \times 10^{14}\,\text{s}^{-1} = 5.55 \times 10^{14}\,\text{Hz}$$

Thus the minimum frequency absorbed by this material is $5.6 \times 10^{14}\,\text{Hz}$, in the green region of the visible spectrum. This minimum frequency is often referred to as the absorption edge. Higher frequencies are absorbed.

QUESTION

6.4   Many insulators are transparent, that is, they do not absorb visible light. The highest frequency of visible light is about $7.5 \times 10^{14}\,\text{Hz}$. Show that the minimum band gap for an insulator to be transparent is about 3.1 eV ($1\,\text{eV} = 1.6 \times 10^{-19}\,\text{J}$).

OPTICAL PROPERTIES

Bands in metals

Metals are opaque; infrared and visible radiation cannot pass through them. The conduction electrons are in a partially filled band. Fig 6.6(b) illustrates the way in which even low-energy photons are absorbed. Vacant states are readily available within the conduction band. High-energy photons may not be absorbed – metals such as sodium are transparent to ultraviolet radiation. Thin metal foils are also transparent to γ-rays and X-rays.

If an electron returns to a lower energy state, it emits a photon. This happens readily in metals, and is the reason why they reflect light and why they are silvery.

So far, we have only considered the way in which the idea of energy bands can help to explain the absorption and emission of light by different types of materials. In Chapter 7, we will extend this picture to give an explanation of electrical conduction and insulation in terms of electron energy bands.

Scattering of light

Some insulators, which we might expect to be transparent, are opaque for a different reason. A clue to this may be found if we think about the way in which a car windscreen shatters – a clear sheet of glass becomes white and opaque. Each individual 'grain' of glass is transparent, but light is scattered at the cracks, the interfaces between the grains.

Similarly, a transparent blue crystal of copper sulphate becomes a white powder when crushed. Many polycrystalline materials, including the glass ceramics referred to in Chapter 3, are opaque (and usually white) for this reason.

Some polymers, such as polythene and nylon, have a milky white translucent appearance – they consist of a mixture of amorphous and crystalline regions. The light scatters at boundaries between these regions. This has been discussed in Section 2.3 above.

QUESTIONS

In the following questions you will need the values $h = 6.63 \times 10^{-34}$ J s and $c = 3 \times 10^8$ m s^{-1}

6.5 Pure silica glass will transmit visible and ultraviolet light down to about 200 nm. Borosilicate glass will transmit down to 300 nm. Soda-lime glass used as windows transmits down to 350 nm. Calculate the energies of the most energetic photons that will be transmitted through each of these glasses. What does this information tell you about the energy bands in each of these materials?

6.6 Explain briefly, in terms of electron energy bands, why many insulators are transparent. Porcelain is used as an insulator in the electrical industry, and yet it is white. Explain why this is so.

6.7 The energy gap in sulphur is 2.2 eV (3.52×10^{-19} J). Sulphur is yellow. How are these two facts related?

6.8 Fig 6.7 shows the energy bands for a particular insulating material. Would this material absorb light of wavelength **(a)** 500 nm and **(b)** 800 nm?

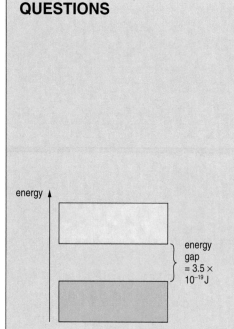

Fig 6.7

6.3 CASE STUDY: OPTICAL FIBRE COMMUNICATIONS

Fig 6.8 Installing optical fibre telephone lines.

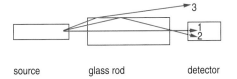

source   glass rod   detector

Fig 6.9 Light rays along a glass rod.

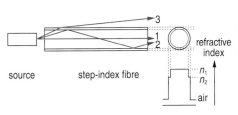

source   step-index fibre

Fig 6.10 Light rays along a step-index fibre, showing its refractive index profile.

Background

You probably know that much of Britain's telephone system is being converted to operate using optical fibres – see Fig 6.8. Telephone messages are transmitted using light as a carrier, along glass fibres, which may be 100 km or more in length. A spoken telephone message has a range of frequencies (bandwidth) of $\sim 10^4$ Hz. Since the frequency of light is high ($\sim 10^{14}$ Hz), a single ray of light may carry many thousands or even millions of low-frequency telephone conversations.

In this case study, we will look at the principles of transmission along optical fibres, the materials used, how they are made, and the solid-state devices used for sending and receiving signals.

Transmission along a fibre

If a light beam is shone directly into a glass rod, it will travel straight along the axis of the rod, and emerge at the other end – see Fig 6.9, ray 1. However, if the ray is not exactly parallel to the axis, two things may happen. In the figure, ray 2 is slightly off-axis, and reflects internally. Ray 3 is at such an angle to the surface that it emerges from the glass and will not be detected at the other end.

Ray 2 has suffered **total internal reflection** at the glass/air interface. Its angle of incidence at the interface is greater than the **critical angle**. (You should be familiar with both of these terms.)

The critical angle θ_c is related to the refractive indices of the media by

$$\sin \theta_c = n_1 / n_2 \qquad (6.1)$$

where, in Fig 6.9, n_1 is the refractive index of air, and n_2 is the refractive index of the glass.

1. Use equation (6.1) to show that, for a glass of refractive index 1.5, the critical angle at a glass/air interface is approximately 42°.

In practice, glass fibres are made of two different glasses, having different refractive indices. A **step-index fibre** has a cylindrical core made of glass of higher refractive index, surrounded by a cladding of lower-index glass – see Fig 6.10. Ray 2 reflects at the interface between core and cladding.

2. Consider Fig 6.10. What can you say about the distances travelled by rays 1 and 2? What effect does this have on their times of arrival at the detector?

A ray travelling along the axis of the fibre travels the shortest distance and thus takes the shortest time to reach the end of the fibre. Any ray that is not precisely parallel to the axis will bounce along from side to side inside the fibre and will take longer to reach the end. This effect has important consequences, since it means that a short-duration pulse of light arrives spread out at the detector.

3. **(a)** Suppose that the ratio of refractive indices of core and cladding is $n_2/n_1 = 1.01$. Show, using equation (6.1), that the critical angle is 82°.

   (b) If the core material has refractive index 1.40, calculate the speed of rays 1 and 2.

   (c) Suppose that the cable is 100 km long, and the core is 50 μm in diameter. If ray 2 has an angle of incidence of 82°, how far does it travel between one end of the cable and the other? How many times is it reflected?

   (d) How much longer does it take ray 2 to travel along the cable than ray 1?

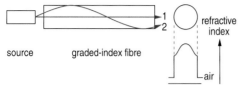

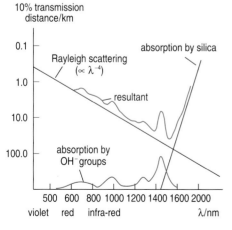

Fig 6.11 Light rays along a graded-index fibre, showing its refractive index profile.

This spreading out, or **dispersion**, of a pulse of light is unacceptable. It is reduced by using core and cladding with similar refractive indices. The critical angle is thus high, and only rays travelling close to the axis are transmitted.

There is another interesting way in which this dispersion may be overcome. Fibres are made with a refractive index that varies between the centre and the outside – **graded-index fibres**. The variation of the refractive index across the diameter is called the refractive index profile of the fibre, and is shown for a graded-index fibre in Fig 6.11.

The rays travel slowest along the centre of the fibre where the refractive index is highest. Hence, although ray 2 has travelled further than ray 1, its average speed is greater, and the two rays reach the end of the fibre approximately simultaneously.

In practice, it is found that the dispersion of a 100 km graded-index fibre may be as little as 0.01 to 0.1 μs. Compare this with the dispersion of a step-index fibre, which you calculated above in question 3(d); the answer to that calculation is 4.6 μs.

Transmission

Of course, if light rays are to be transmitted over such great distances, we must use a material that does not absorb the light. We will now look in some detail at the problem of transmitting light over long distances through glass.

We will express the absorption of light by glass in terms of its '10% transmission distance', the thickness (or length) of material that absorbs 90% of the light and transmits the remaining 10%. (The intensity of light decreases exponentially as it passes down the fibre.)

4. What features of the microstructure of the glass might result in non-transmission of light? You should be able to suggest several.

If you look at a sheet of window glass edge-on, or a glass rod along its length, you will see that it is coloured. This colour, usually blue or green, arises from the presence of metallic impurities, which absorb some of the light passing through. Table 6.1 shows the absorption by impurity ions in glass. Notice that the amount of absorption depends on the glass being used. Notice also the large effect that one part per million of an impurity ion may have – Cr in silica glass is particularly dramatic.

Table 6.1 Absorption by impurities in different types of glass at 850 nm for impurity concentrations of one part per million

Impurity	10% transmission distance/km	
	Borosilicate glass (pyrex)	Silica glass
Fe	2.0	0.08
Cu	0.02	0.45
Cr	0.4	0.01
Ni	0.05	0.37
OH	0.67	1.0

5. Which impurity is most strongly absorbing in borosilicate glass? Which is least absorbing?

Once metallic impurities and other imperfections have been removed from the glass, there are still limitations to the transmission of light. The three most important factors are Rayleigh scattering, absorption by the fibre material, and absorption by OH⁻ ions trapped in the glass. The extent of absorption depends on the wavelength of light being used – see Fig 6.12.

Minute fluctuations in the density of the glass give rise to the

Fig 6.12 Factors reducing light transmission along optical fibres.

OPTICAL PROPERTIES

phenomenon known as **Rayleigh scattering**. The amount of scattering is inversely proportional to the fourth power of the wavelength (i.e. scattering $\propto \lambda^{-4}$). Hence long wavelengths (red and infrared) are scattered least. You should be able to find out why the sky is blue and the setting Sun is red – a result of Rayleigh scattering.

The fibre material is usually silica. The Si–O bonds absorb very long-wavelength infrared radiation.

It is impossible to exclude all traces of water vapour from the glass production process. Consequently, hydroxyl (OH^-) ions are present. Their absorption spectrum has a peak at 1400 nm – see Fig 6.12. The figure also shows the combined effect of all three mechanisms. Study this figure, and answer the following questions.

6. Which mechanism reduces transmission most significantly at far-infrared wavelengths?

7. Many operational systems use light of wavelength 850 nm. Which mechanism is most significant at this wavelength?

8. Development engineers talk of 'windows' at 1300 nm and 1550 nm. Why are these wavelengths more likely to be used than 1400 nm in second-generation fibre systems?

9. If it were possible to remove all traces of OH^- ions from the glass, what wavelength would be most suitable for use in fibre systems? What would the 10% transmission distance be at this wavelength?

You will have observed from Fig 6.12 that silica absorption dominates at long wavelengths, Rayleigh scattering at short wavelengths. A wavelength of 1400 nm is unsuitable as this is the peak absorption by hydroxyl ions. If these ions are removed, the best wavelength would be about 1550 nm, where the 10% transmission distance is about 70 km. This wavelength is in the infrared region of the electromagnetic spectrum.

Clearly, the composition of material used for optical fibres is crucial. It determines the transmission of light, and the most suitable wavelengths to be used in practice.

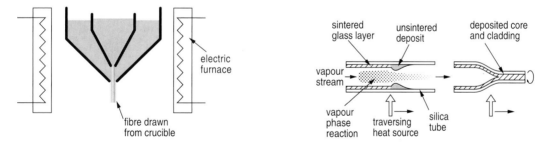

Fig 6.13 Fabrication of optical fibres: **(a)** double crucible method; **(b)** chemical vapour deposition.

Fibre fabrication

There are two principal methods used for manufacturing optical fibres; they are illustrated in Fig 6.13.

The double crucible method is used primarily for step-index fibres. The core material is contained in the inner crucible and the cladding in the outer. The crucibles are made from ultra-pure platinum to avoid contamination. The fibre is extruded through concentric nozzles.

The chemical vapour deposition method is used for graded-index fibres. Silicon tetrachloride ($SiCl_4$) gas is passed into a heated high-purity silica tube, where it reacts with oxygen to form silica (SiO_2), which deposits on the wall of the tube. By gradually increasing the concentration of a dopant, such as germanium tetrachloride ($GeCl_4$), which reacts to form germania

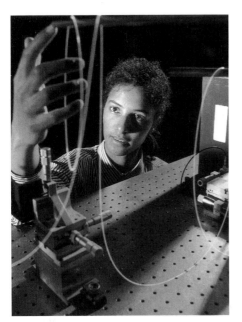

Fig 6.14 Manufacturing optical fibres.

(GeO$_2$), the refractive index of the glass is made to increase. The resulting tube is collapsed to form a solid rod of glass with high refractive index at the centre. This 'preform' is pulled out into a long fibre and reeled onto a drum – see Fig 6.14.

Light sources and detectors

Light-emitting diodes may be used as light sources for transmitting signals along optical fibres. Their principal disadvantages are their low power output (less than 1 mW) and the spread of frequencies they produce (typically 30–40 nm). Different frequencies travel at different speeds, and this leads to spectral dispersion of the signal.

Semiconductor lasers provide higher powers (up to 10 mW) and have a spectral spread of 1–2 nm. The construction of one such laser is shown in Fig 6.15. It is rather complex, and we are not concerned with the details. It does show, however, an important application of semiconductor technology, in particular the use of several different doped materials.

Light signals are detected by photodiodes, which are built into a single chip along with the transistor circuitry necessary for amplifying the signal. This detector–amplifier chip may be only a few millimetres across, making for very compact systems.

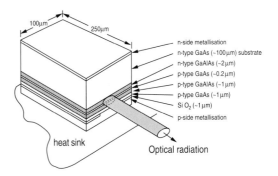

Fig 6.15 A solid-state laser used for transmitting light along optical fibres. Note the tiny dimensions.

Because the intensity of the light signal decreases as it is gradually absorbed along the length of a fibre optic cable, it is necessary to incorporate detector–amplifier–laser repeater stations every 100 km or so.

10. Typically, a laser transmitter launches about 1 mW of optical power into a fibre. A detector requires about 10 nW for detection. If the fibre has a 10% transmission distance of 20 km, how long can it be if the signal is to be detectable? (The intensity of the signal decreases to one-tenth of its original value in 20 km.)

INVESTIGATION

Hazard warning
Wear eye protection when you do this.

You can make your own optical fibres by drawing out a glass rod that you have softened in a Bunsen flame. Make a fibre and use it to show that light can be transmitted round corners.

Devise a method for determining the intensity of the light transmitted along the fibre. By making fibres of different lengths, you may be able to detect the way in which the intensity decreases along the fibre.

SUMMARY

The different optical spectra produced by solids, liquids and gases give us information about the electronic structure of these materials. We interpret the spectra of solids in terms of energy bands; these allow us to explain the different optical properties of metals, semiconductors and insulators.

Chapter 7

ELECTRICAL CONDUCTION

People first refined and used metals for their decorative qualities. Gold became a symbol of power. Then other metals came to be used when their mechanical properties were discovered. Iron and bronze implements and weapons replaced stone.

But metals have other properties that we have come to exploit more recently. In particular, metals (and other materials) conduct electricity. Our electrical supply industry relies on the existence of both good conductors and good insulators.

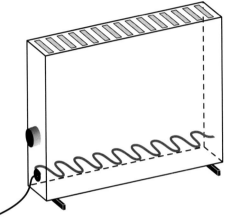

Fig 7.1 What materials are suitable for the element of an electric heater?

LEARNING OBJECTIVES

After studying this chapter you should be able to:

1. define and use the terms 'conductance' and 'conductivity';

2. derive and use the equation for current in a conductor, $I = nAve$;

3. relate the conductivity of metals, semiconductors and insulators to their electron energy band structures;

4. describe how the electrical properties of semiconductors may be modified by doping with impurities;

5. explain the operation of simple electronic devices in terms of changes in electron energy;

6. describe the phenomenon of superconductivity in terms of critical temperature, critical field, critical current density and the Meissner effect.

7.1 CONDUCTANCE AND CONDUCTIVITY

Introduction

Let us think about the selection of suitable materials for a familiar use: an electric heater – Fig 7.1. Consider the heating element of such a heater. The element must be a good conductor. Since the power dissipated $P = V^2/R$, the element must have a fairly low resistance R. But should R increase or decrease with temperature? Think of the consequences of using a material whose resistivity decreases with increasing temperature.

The element must heat up quickly, and must operate at high temperatures in air.

QUESTION

7.1 What properties must the material used for such a heating element have to satisfy these requirements? Think about resistivity and how it changes with temperature; heat capacity; melting point; chemical

---

As is often the case with technological problems, there is more than one solution. In practice, alloys are used in preference to pure metals, as their resistivity is higher. Some elements are made from ceramic materials. Many electric fires have nichrome (alloy) wire elements. Since the wire must be long and thin, it is wound in a spiral around an insulating ceramic support, the design of which is another technological problem.

Some furnaces use silicon carbide, in the form of rod-shaped elements. Since this material is more resistive than nichrome, it can be shorter and fatter, and therefore self-supporting. It can also operate at considerably higher temperatures.

Resistivity and conductivity

To define the resistivity of a material, we consider a cylinder of length l and cross-sectional area A – see Fig 7.2. The **resistance**

$$R = V/I \qquad \text{(units: } \Omega\text{)}$$

of such a cylinder increases with length, and decreases with area. The **resistivity** ρ is thus defined by

$$\rho = RA/l \qquad \text{(units: } \Omega\,\text{m)}$$

Sometimes it is preferable to think in terms of how good a material is at conducting electricity. We therefore define the **conductance** G of a component as the reciprocal of resistance:

$$G = 1/R = I/V \qquad \text{(units: S (siemens), where } 1\,\text{S} = 1\,\Omega^{-1}\text{)}$$

The **conductivity** σ of a material is defined as the reciprocal of resistivity:

$$\sigma = 1/\rho = Gl/A \qquad \text{(units: S\,m}^{-1}\text{)}$$

Electrical resistivity is a property that shows great variation between materials – see Fig 7.3. The best insulator is 10^{23} times as resistive as the best conductor. This means that a range of materials with vastly different electrical properties are available to engineers when designing devices that rely on electrical conduction or insulation. Materials of the desired resistivity can be selected and, as we shall see, it is possible to design materials whose resistivities vary with temperature in different ways.

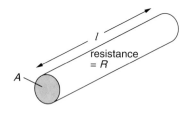

Fig 7.2 The resistance of a conductor depends on its length and cross-sectional area.

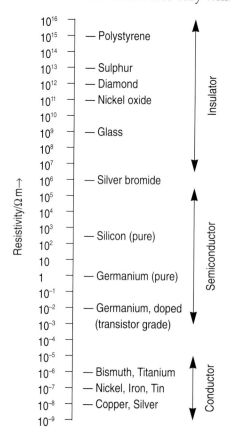

Fig 7.3 The electrical resistivities of materials range over 23 orders of magnitude. (This material property varies more than any other.)

ELECTRICAL CONDUCTION

7.2 Use the information in Fig 7.3 to deduce approximate values for the conductivity of **(a)** polystyrene and **(b)** silver.

7.3 A copper wire is measured and found to be 2.5 m in length; its diameter is 1.0 mm. The conductivity of copper is $6 \times 10^7 \, S \, m^{-1}$. Calculate:

(a) the conductance of the wire;

(b) its resistance.

7.2 ELECTRONS ON THE MOVE

Current in a wire

In an electrical conductor such as a metal, it is a flow of electrons that constitutes a current. We can deduce an expression to relate the current I that flows through a wire to the rate at which electrons move, as follows. We will consider a piece of wire whose length is l and whose cross-sectional area is A, as shown in Fig 7.4. The electrons are moving steadily from left to right, giving rise to a current I from right to left (because electrons have a negative charge).

We picture the electrons as moving at a steady speed v; of course, in practice, they will all move at different speeds, and they will speed up and slow down as a result of collisions, etc. Now, suppose that an electron at the left-hand end of the wire takes time t to reach the other end. Its speed v is then given by

$$v = l/t$$

In time t, all of the electrons within this section of wire will flow out of the wire. If we can work out their total charge, we can deduce an expression for the current I that is flowing. To find the total charge of the electrons in the wire, we work out its volume:

$$\text{volume of wire} = l \times A$$

Now, if n is the concentration of free electrons in the wire (there are n electrons per cubic metre), we have

$$\text{number of electrons in wire} = \text{volume} \times \text{concentration} = n \times l \times A$$

And, since the charge of each electron is e,

$$\text{total charge of electrons in wire} = n \times l \times A \times e$$

The current flowing is this charge divided by the time t:

$$I = (n \times l \times A \times e)/t$$

Since $v = l/t$, this expression simplifies to

$$I = nAve$$

This equation relates the current (a macroscopic quantity) to the properties of electrons (microscopic quantities).

In fact, the velocity v in this equation is the **drift velocity** of the electrons. They move about very fast and randomly in a metal (at speeds of about $10^6 \, m \, s^{-1}$). When they form part of an electric current, they have an additional velocity along the wire, which may only be a fraction of a millimetre per second.

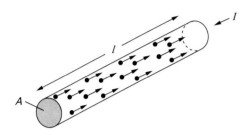

Fig 7.4 Electrons in a metal move in the opposite direction to the flow of current.

Calculate the drift velocity of the free electrons in a piece of copper wire, 1 mm in diameter, when a current of 1 A flows. The concentration of free electrons in copper is $n = 10^{29} \, \text{m}^{-3}$

Solution

Rearranging the equation

$$I = nAve$$

gives

$$v = I/(nAe)$$

Substituting gives

$$v = 1/[10^{29} \times \pi \times (0.5 \times 10^{-3})^2 \times 1.6 \times 10^{-19}] = 8.0 \times 10^{-5} \, \text{m s}^{-1}$$

So the drift velocity of the electrons is about $0.08 \, \text{mm s}^{-1}$, not very fast for this typical current.

7.4 Calculate the drift velocity of electrons in a semiconductor slice whose cross-section is 1 mm × 3 mm, when a current of 5 mA flows. The semiconductor has a free-electron concentration of $5 \times 10^{22} \, \text{m}^{-3}$.

7.5 In measurements of electrons in a piece of semiconductor using the Hall effect (see Chapter 9), it was found that their drift velocity was $2.4 \, \text{m s}^{-1}$. The semiconductor measured 10 mm × 0.5 mm, and the current flowing was 0.02 A. Deduce the concentration of free electrons in the material.

Current density

It is sometimes more useful to write the equation $I = nAve$ in the form

$$J = nev$$

where $J = I/A$ is the **current density**. The quantities on the right-hand side are dependent on the material under consideration. If we wish to change the current density, we must think about the factors that determine n and v, and even consider materials in which the current is not of electrons but of other charged particles.

In the next section, we will look at electrical conduction in different materials, and see how our observations can be explained in terms of band theory and these equations.

7.3 CONDUCTION AND BAND THEORY

The electrons in the conduction band of any material are more or less free to move through the solid under the influence of an electric field. Good conductors like copper have more electrons in the conduction band than a poorer conductor like bismuth. In other words, copper has a higher value of n than bismuth. An insulator like diamond has virtually no electrons in the conduction band at room temperature.

Increasing the temperature results in increased atomic vibrations. Adding impurities, and introducing other lattice defects such as grain boundaries, dislocations and vacancies, provides obstacles to the free movement of electrons. All these effects reduce the drift velocity of the electrons, and hence increase the resistivity of a conductor.

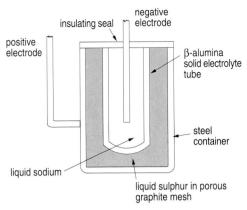

Fig 7.5 Schematic diagram of a sodium–sulphur cell.

Insulators

At high temperatures, insulators may become conducting. Often, this is because ions, rather than electrons, become free to move through the solid. As a solid is heated, increased thermal vibration results in more vacancies in the structure. Ions can travel through the material by moving to occupy nearby vacancies, or they may move along grain boundaries.

Materials with high ionic conductivity are likely to form the basis of a new generation of storage batteries for electric vehicles. One promising system is the sodium–sulphur cell, shown diagrammatically in Fig 7.5. The electrolyte separating the sodium and sulphur is a ceramic (β-alumina, $Na_2Al_{22}O_{34}$). Sodium ions pass very readily through this material at 300 °C. The battery therefore has low internal resistance; it can provide an e.m.f. of 2.3 V.

Semiconductors

Materials such as silicon (Si) or gallium arsenide (GaAs) are semiconductors; as we have seen in Chapter 6, they have a small forbidden energy gap, and at temperatures above 0 K some electrons have enough energy to enter the conduction band. These electrons can take part in the conduction process.

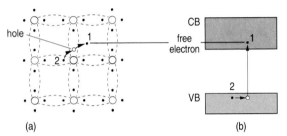

Fig 7.6 **(a)** A two-dimensional representation of the silicon crystal. Electron 1 breaks free, leaving a hole. Electron 2 moves to occupy the hole. The hole effectively moves in the opposite direction. **(b)** Energy band representation of the same process.

Vacancies have been left behind in the valence band. These are referred to as **holes**, and they too can take part in the conduction process. Fig 7.6(a) shows how.

The four outermost electrons of each silicon atom are involved in bonding with neighbouring atoms. A single electron has broken away from one bond. It moves off through the structure, leaving a hole. A second electron from an adjacent bond can now move into this hole. The hole disappears, but a new hole appears at the point where the second electron was initially. The hole appears to have moved. It behaves like a mobile positive charge, since it moves in the opposite direction to the electrons. The current flow consists of electrons and holes moving in opposite directions.

This may also be illustrated using the energy band picture – Fig 7.6(b). Electron 1 moves up to the conduction band. Electron 2 moves in to fill the resulting hole. These pictures represent the same process; one shows what is happening in spatial terms, the other in energy terms.

This type of material is called an **intrinsic semiconductor**, since the ability to conduct is a property of the material itself. As the temperature increases, more and more electrons break free in this way. The free-electron concentration n increases, and so the material becomes a better conductor. This is in contrast to metals, whose resistance increases with increasing temperature.

Electronic devices

Thermistors (thermal resistors) are semiconductor devices whose resistance increases or decreases rapidly with temperature – they are known as positive and negative temperature coefficient thermistors respectively. In the investigation, you can look at the way in which the resistances of these

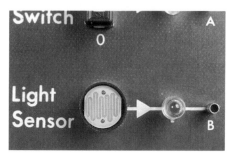

Fig 7.7 A light-dependent resistor (LDR) is a device based on a semiconductor material.

devices vary with temperature.

Detectors of infrared radiation are also based on semiconductors. Since the frequency of the radiation is low (down to 3×10^{13} Hz), the material chosen must have a narrow energy gap.

A **light-dependent resistor** (LDR), such as the ORP-12 (Fig 7.7), is based on a semiconducting material, usually cadmium sulphide. In the dark, its resistance is ~10 MΩ. When light falls on it, its resistance falls to 1 kΩ or lower.

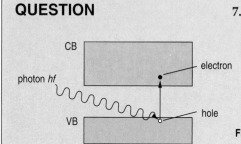

QUESTION

7.6 Fig 7.8 shows the energy band picture of what happens when light falls on the material of a light-dependent resistor. Use this diagram as the basis of an explanation of the way in which light causes an LDR to conduct.

Fig 7.8 How does light cause an increase in the conductivity of this semiconductor?

INVESTIGATION

Thermistors

Thermistors are devices made from semiconducting materials whose resistance changes considerably over a narrow range of temperature. If their resistance increases as temperature increases, they are known as positive temperature coefficient (PTC) types; if their resistance decreases as temperature increases, they are known as negative temperature coefficient (NTC) types. Thermistors may be used to measure temperature and to protect circuits from damage due to heating effects.

The aim of this investigation is to measure the resistance of NTC and PTC thermistors over a range of temperatures. The following thermistors are suitable: NTC thermistor, RS 151-079 or RS 151-108; PTC thermistor, RS 158-272.

1. Devise an appropriate circuit to measure the current through the thermistor when a constant p.d. of 2 V is maintained across it.

2. Measure the current through the device at suitable temperature intervals between room temperature and 100 °C. (You can maintain water at a constant temperature of your choice using a Thermos flask.)

3. Plot a graph of resistance against temperature for each type of thermistor.

4. Try to explain what is happening as the temperature rises, in terms of the equation $J = nev$.

7.4 DOPED SEMICONDUCTORS

Intrinsic semiconductors have resistivities that are typically $1\,\Omega$ m or greater. Many applications, such as transistors and integrated circuits, use materials that are better conductors than this, but not as highly conducting as metals. Doped semiconductors are used. They are an example of the way in which a material with the desired properties can be achieved by controlling the level of defects in the structure.

Doping is achieved by adding small amounts of impurities to an intrinsic semiconductor; for example, aluminium or phosphorus may be added to silicon. The concentration is typically 100 to 1000 parts per million. The result is called an **extrinsic semiconductor**.

Again, we can describe the effect of the presence of impurities using two pictures, one showing the crystal structure and the other the energy bands – parts (a) and (b) respectively in Figs 7.9 and 7.10.

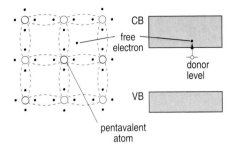

Fig 7.9 An n-type semiconductor. The outermost electron of the pentavalent atom is only weakly bound. It easily breaks free, and can move throughout the material.

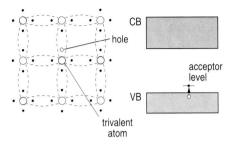

Fig 7.10 A p-type semiconductor. An electron may move into the hole associated with the trivalent atom. The hole may subsequently move through the material, increasing its conductivity.

n-type

A phosphorus atom has one more electron than a silicon atom – look at the Periodic Table. Of its five outermost electrons, four are involved in bonding with neighbouring silicon atoms, and the fifth electron can break free to move through the crystal – Fig 7.9(a). A positively charged phosphorus ion is left behind, unable to move through the material. An impurity of this kind is called a donor, since it donates a conduction electron. There are still intrinsic electrons and holes present in relatively small numbers; the majority carriers are electrons, and the material is called n-type, since the electrons are negatively charged.

The energy band picture (Fig 7.9(b)) shows the same process. The extra electron of the phosphorus atom is only weakly bonded; its energy is just below the conduction band. Little thermal energy is required for it to be promoted. This level is called a **donor level**.

p-type

An aluminium atom has one less electron than a silicon atom in its outer shell. When substituted in a silicon crystal, it has only three electrons available for bonding with silicon atoms. There is effectively a hole at the aluminium atom – Fig 7.10(a). An electron from a neighbouring silicon atom may gain enough energy to enter the hole; the hole has thus moved to the silicon atom, and the material conducts.

Fig 7.10(b) shows the energy band picture of this process. The aluminium atom provides an additional energy level (the **acceptor level**) just above the valence band. Electrons promoted to this level leave behind a hole. The material conducts by means of movement of holes, as described for intrinsic semiconductors. A p-type semiconductor results. The majority carriers are holes, which act as if they have a positive charge.

By choosing a suitable intrinsic semiconductor, we can achieve materials with large or small energy gaps; and by doping with suitable impurities, we can achieve high or low carrier concentrations, of holes or electrons.

More devices

The **p–n junction diode** and the various kinds of **transistor** are based on doped semiconductors; the way they work is beyond our present scope.

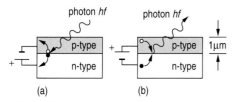

(a)   (b)

Fig 7.11 Two p–n junction devices: **(a)** a photodiode; **(b)** a light-emitting diode.

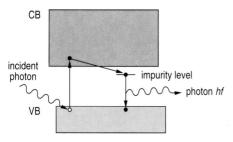

Fig 7.12 The action of a phosphorescent material.

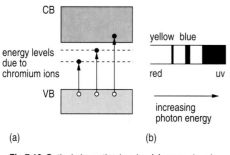

(a)   (b)

Fig 7.13 Optical absorption in ruby: **(a)** energy bands; **(b)** the corresponding optical absorption spectrum.

In order to create an electron–hole pair, energy must be supplied. In a **photodiode**, light is shone on the p-side of a p–n junction diode. Electron–hole pairs are created, and contribute to the current flowing – see Fig 7.11(a).

A **light-emitting diode** (LED) uses the principle in reverse. Electrons meet holes at a p–n junction, and light is emitted as the two recombine – Fig 7.11(b). Different semiconductors with different dopants may be chosen to give different colours of LED.

Some semiconductors and other materials show **phosphorescence**; that is, they glow for a short time after light or electrons have been shone on them. Incident light causes electrons to be promoted to the conduction band. Some electrons fall into an impurity level high up in the energy gap. They are slow to return to the valence band; it may be seconds or longer before they do so, emitting radiation as they fall – see Fig 7.12. Phosphorescent materials are used on radar screens, to provide an image that lasts for several seconds before replenishing.

Gemstones and lasers

Many gemstones are transparent insulators containing small amounts of impurities, and are comparable to doped semiconductors. Some are based on the ceramic alumina, Al_2O_3. Titanium impurity gives a clear blue sapphire, magnesium gives yellow sapphire, and chromium gives red ruby. How do these colours arise?

Let us consider ruby. Chromium ions in the alumina crystal introduce two additional energy levels into the energy gap of the alumina – see Fig 7.13(a). The resulting absorption spectrum is shown in Fig 7.13(b).

Ruby is the basis of a very important kind of laser. Intense white light is shone on a ruby crystal. Electrons gain energy, rise to the conduction band, and then fall to the chromium energy levels. When they simultaneously return to the valence band, they emit intense visible light, which is the basis of the laser.

QUESTION

7.7 Can you explain how the two parts of Fig 7.13 are connected? Try to answer the following questions:

(a) Which part of the absorption spectrum is due to electrons being promoted between the valence and conduction bands?

(b) Which part is due to electrons entering the chromium ion levels?

(c) Yellow and blue light are being absorbed. Why does the crystal

---

Conducting polymers

We tend to think of polymers as insulators. In fact, a number of familiar polymers have resistivities in the range 10^{13} to $10^{15}\,\Omega\,m$. This is why they can be used in the manufacture of light fittings, switches, electric cables, etc. However, a novel group of polymers is being developed that have resistivities comparable with those of semiconductors and metals.

The origin of electrical conduction in these materials is intimately linked to the type of bonding in their molecules. The structural feature responsible for conduction in these polymers is also found in graphite – a non-metallic conductor with which you are familiar. Polyethyne, the first conducting polymer to be discovered, was synthesised by polymerising ethyne (acetylene, C_2H_2). Polyethyne differs from polyethene in the number of hydrogen atoms attached to each carbon atom in the chain; it is one in

ELECTRICAL CONDUCTION

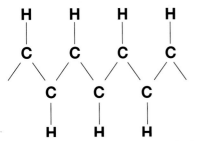

Fig 7.14 Skeletal arrangement of atoms in polyethyne.

polyethyne and two in polyethene. We will now consider how electrical conduction is possible in such covalently bonded materials.

Each carbon atom has four electrons available for forming bonds with other atoms. When the ethyne monomer units polymerise, long planar zigzag molecules are formed; one type is shown in Fig 7.14.

You will see that in this structure only three of the four bonding electrons of each carbon atom are needed to form the molecular chain. In such a planar structure, the remaining electron associated with each atom can move freely along the carbon chain. Such electrons are said to be **delocalised**. They have a freedom of movement analogous to that of electrons in metals and can be said to occupy a partially filled conduction band. Bonds between atoms that comprise the chain are covalent. Electrons in the bonds are localised and occupy the valence band.

In practice, irregularities in the polymerisation process disrupt the perfect planarity of atoms and make conduction along the entire length of the chain impossible. The conductivity of a sample of polyethyne with imperfections is comparable with that of semiconductors.

It is possible, however, by means of chemical reactions, either to add extra electrons or to remove electrons from the conduction band. Lengths of chain treated in this way become respectively either n-type or p-type semiconductors. This opens up the exciting prospect of molecular and semiconducting devices.

Conducting polymers are not yet used in any commercial applications. At present the materials produced are not stable over long periods of time – they are attacked by atmospheric oxygen – and the rigidity of their planar structure makes them difficult to fabricate. Their study is an exciting area of active research in which you, as a future materials scientist, could participate.

ASSIGNMENT

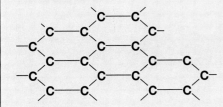

Fig 7.15 Arrangement of covalent bonds in graphite.

Polyethyne

Polyethyne, like graphite, is black, unlike the non-conducting polymers that you have encountered. The bonding between the carbon atoms in polyethyne is similar to that in graphite – Fig 7.15. The carbon atoms in graphite form continuous planar sheets.

7.8   Can you explain why polyethyne is black from what you know of band theory and its relationship to optical properties?

7.9   Can you explain why graphite is a better conductor?

QUESTIONS

7.10 The energy gap in silicon is $\approx 1.76 \times 10^{-19}$ J. Silicon is opaque and reflective like a metal, yet its resistivity is 10^{10} times greater than most metals at room temperature. Explain why this is so.

7.11 The resistance of a metal increases with increasing temperature, while the resistances of many semiconductors decrease. Explain this difference; your answer should refer to the equation $J = nev$.

7.12 A slab of semiconductor material is connected across the terminals of a microammeter. One end of the material is heated, the other cooled. A current is found to flow through the meter.

(a)   Explain what effect heating has on the concentration of conduction electrons in the material.

(b)   Explain why a current flows.

(c)   What difference would you expect to observe if p-type and n-type doped materials were used?

7.5 THE HALL EFFECT

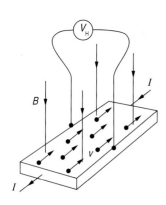

Fig 7.16 The Hall effect: a current flows through a magnetic field, and a voltage appears at 90° to both.

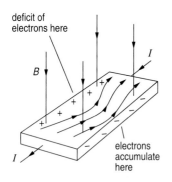

Fig 7.17 The Hall effect arises as a consequence of the magnetic force on moving electrons.

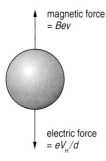

Fig 7.18 Electric and magnetic forces on the electron are balanced.

The Hall effect is a useful effect for two reasons: it allows us to determine whether the particles that are moving in a conductor are positively or negatively charged (i.e. holes or electrons); and it allows us to measure their concentration n.

To observe the Hall effect, we place a piece of current-carrying material in a magnetic field. As the current flows along the material, a voltage appears across it. Fig 7.16 shows the geometry of this arrangement.

For the effect to be a maximum, the magnetic flux must be at right angles to the current. The voltage that appears across the material is called the **Hall voltage** V_H.

Origin of the effect

We will picture the current in Fig 7.16 as a flow of electrons, which are negatively charged. As they move through the magnetic field, they experience a force at right angles to both B and their velocity v. The direction of the force is given by Fleming's left-hand rule. Fig 7.17 shows the result: electrons are deflected to one side of the material.

The piling-up of electrons at one side leaves a deficit of electrons at the other. Consequently, one side acquires a negative charge while the other side becomes positively charged. A voltmeter connected between the two sides will detect a potential difference between them. This is the Hall voltage.

If we think about an individual electron passing through the material, it will experience two forces. One force is the magnetic force Bev; the other is the electric force eV_H/d caused by the Hall voltage; any electron passing through the material is repelled by the electrons that have accumulated at the side. Fig 7.18 shows these two forces. The forces are balanced, and so we can conclude that

$$Bev = eV_H/d \tag{7.1}$$

or

$$V_H = Bvd \tag{7.2}$$

We can now combine this equation with $I = nAve$ to eliminate v:

$$V_H = BId/nAe \tag{7.3}$$

Since $A = d \times t$, this simplifies to

$$V_H = BI/net \tag{7.4}$$

We will now examine this expression, and see what the Hall effect can tell us.

Dependence on *B* and *I*

The Hall voltage is proportional to the magnetic flux density B. This means that the Hall effect can be used to measure flux density. A Hall probe (Fig 7.19) does this. A small current flows through a slice of semiconducting material. When the probe is positioned at right angles to the flux, the Hall voltage appears across it, and is measured using a voltmeter. The probe has to be calibrated by placing it in a known field.

A Hall probe can be very sensitive; you can use it to measure the Earth's magnetic flux density. Position it so that the Earth's flux passes directly through the probe, and then turn it rapidly through 180°. The voltage will reverse, because the flux through the probe has been reversed.

To give a significant voltage, the current through the probe must be as large as possible, since V_H is proportional to I. In practice, this is limited by the fact that the current tends to heat up the semiconductor through which it is flowing. A few milliamps is all that can be safely used.

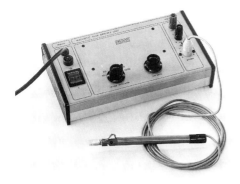

Fig 7.19 A Hall probe is a sensitive device for measuring magnetic fields.

Influence of *n* and *e*

In a Hall probe, the material used is a semiconductor. This is because the concentration n of free electrons is considerably lower than in metals. The equation $V_H = BI/net$ shows that the Hall voltage is inversely proportional to n; hence the smaller the value of n, the greater the Hall voltage.

The charge on the electrons is also significant. In a p-type semiconductor, the current consists chiefly of a flow of holes, which are positively charged. From the equation for V_H, it follows that the sign of the Hall voltage will be reversed when a p-type material is used, compared with an n-type material. Hence the Hall effect provides us with a tool to determine the concentration n and the sign of the charge of the moving particles.

QUESTIONS

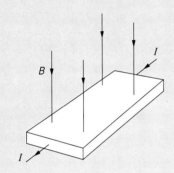

Fig 7.20 The Hall effect in a p-type semiconductor.

7.13 (a) Calculate the Hall voltage induced across a slice of semiconductor 0.1 mm thick by a field of flux density 0.5 T when a current of 5 mA flows through it. The semiconductor has a free-electron concentration of 10^{22} m^{-3}. (Electron charge $e = 1.6 \times 10^{-19}$ C.)

(b) Suppose that a slice of copper had been used instead of the semiconductor. Explain why this would be an unsuitable choice of material for a Hall probe. (Free-electron concentration in copper = 10^{29} m^{-3}.)

7.14 The Hall effect can be used to decide whether the moving charges in a piece of semiconductor are electrons or holes. To illustrate this, proceed as follows:

(a) Make a copy of Fig 7.20, which is the same as Fig 7.17, but in this case the slice consists of p-type material.

(b) Show the flow of holes, which constitutes the current.

(c) Determine the direction in which the holes will be deflected by the magnetic field.

(d) Which side of the slice will become positively charged? Which will become negative? What can you conclude?

7.15 Explain how you could use the Hall effect to determine the concentration of free electrons in a slice of n-type semiconductor. What measurements would you need to make?

INVESTIGATION

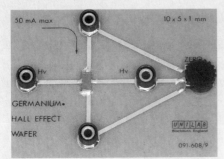

Fig 7.21 A slice of doped germanium mounted with terminals for current and Hall voltage.

The Hall effect

You can use a slice of semiconductor like that shown in Fig 7.21 to investigate the Hall effect. The slice of doped germanium is mounted so that two terminals are available for passing current through the slice, and the other two can be used to measure the Hall voltage. By making suitable measurements, you can determine the concentration of free charges, and decide whether they are electrons or holes.

7.6 SUPER-CONDUCTORS

Fig 7.22 Kamerlingh Onnes (left), discoverer of superconductivity, with van der Waals.

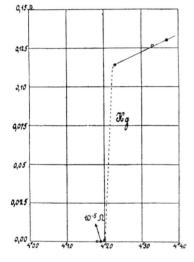

Fig 7.23 The first measurements to show superconductivity: Onnes's results for the resistance of a mercury wire at low temperatures.

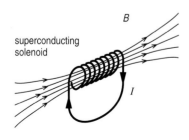

Fig 7.24 A current can flow for ever round a superconducting coil.

Superconductivity is a fascinating phenomenon, and one whose applications are becoming increasingly important. It is found that, when some materials are cooled down, they reach a temperature at which their electrical resistance suddenly drops to zero. The first such materials to be discovered became superconducting at very low temperatures, close to absolute zero. It was the ability to liquefy helium that made it possible to reach these temperatures, and gave rise to the discovery of superconductivity.

Zero resistance

Helium becomes a liquid when cooled to 4.2 K, the lowest temperature of any gas. This was first achieved by the Dutch physicist Kamerlingh Onnes (Fig 7.22) in 1908. The main interest in producing liquid helium was in order to use it as a refrigerant, so that the properties of materials could be studied at temperatures approaching 0 K.

Onnes went on to investigate how the resistance of different metals changed as the temperature was lowered. For most metals, there is a steady decrease in resistance with decreasing temperature. However, when measurements were made on mercury, a striking result was obtained. Onnes's results are shown in Fig 7.23. At a temperature slightly above 4.2 K, the resistance of the mercury dropped dramatically. From the graph, you can see that the resistance dropped from about 0.11 Ω to about 10^{-5} Ω in the space of a few hundredths of a degree.

In fact, we now know that the resistance of such a superconducting metal is actually zero, but Onnes could not achieve the necessary precision to be sure of this. When a metal becomes superconducting, its resistance to the flow of current completely disappears. The temperature at which this occurs is known as the **critical temperature**, T_c. When Onnes published his results in 1911, he was able to conclude that the resistance of mercury fell by a factor of ten orders of magnitude (10^{10}) at the critical temperature.

To show that the resistance of a superconducting metal is truly zero, it can be made into a simple coil (Fig 7.24). If a current is made to flow in the coil, it acts as a solenoid to produce a magnetic field. This field can be detected outside the coil, and it is found that the current can flow for years without the magnetic field showing any measurable decrease. There is absolutely no resistance to the flow of current.

More superconductors

Because of the obvious importance of materials that have no electrical resistance, a great deal of effort was put into finding more examples. Table 7.1 lists some superconducting metals, together with their critical temperatures. There are many other metals that never show superconductivity, no matter to what temperature they are cooled – copper, silver and gold, for example.

Table 7.1 Critical temperatures and magnetic flux densities for some superconducting metals

Element	Critical temperature, T_c/K	Critical flux density, B_c/mT
aluminium	1.12	11
indium	3.41	28
lead	7.20	80
niobium	9.25	206
tin	3.72	31
niobium–tin	18.05	
niobium–aluminium	17.5	

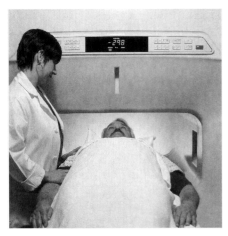

Fig 7.25 This magnetic resonance imaging body scanner uses large superconducting magnets to produce the necessary magnetic field.

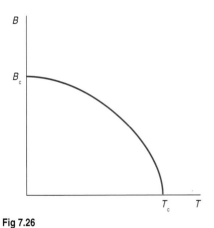

Fig 7.26

Table 7.1 also includes some metallic compounds, which were found to become superconducting at higher critical temperatures than for pure metals.

The problem with superconductivity was that low temperatures were needed to make ordinary metals become superconducting. This meant that liquid helium was needed; helium is a rare element, and it is expensive to buy and to liquefy. Consequently, it was not practicable to use superconductors for large-scale applications. For example, it would be highly desirable to transmit electrical power along superconducting power lines, because a significant fraction of the power is wasted in heating the wires, but this is entirely unfeasible.

As liquid helium has become more readily available, it has become possible to use superconductors in some important applications, such as the giant superconducting magnets used in magnetic resonance body scanners – see Fig 7.25.

Superconductors and magnetism

Superconductivity is destroyed by a sufficiently strong magnetic field. This is another frustrating feature of superconductivity, since one of its most valuable applications is in the production of strong magnetic fields. If the current through a superconducting solenoid is increased, the magnetic field increases. However, when the field strength reaches a certain value, the resistance of the superconductor returns, and the current can no longer flow.

Measurements show that the field strength at which this occurs increases as the temperature drops below the critical temperature. Fig 7.26 shows that, just below the critical temperature, a small magnetic field is enough. At absolute zero, the superconductor can withstand a stronger field. This is called the **critical flux density** B_c; values are shown in Table 7.1. In any field stronger than B_c the superconductor returns to its normal, resistive state.

It is also found that superconductors can only carry a limited current; if the current density is increased above a certain value, called the **critical current density** J_c, the material again loses its superconductivity and becomes resistive. The magnetic field produced by the current itself exceeds the critical flux density.

QUESTIONS

7.16 (a) It would be useful if we could transmit electrical power along superconducting transmission lines. Why would this be desirable?

(b) Unfortunately, this is unlikely ever to be practicable. Explain why, referring to 'critical temperature', 'critical current density' and 'cost'.

7.17 There is a relationship between the critical temperature T_c and the critical flux density B_c of a superconductor. Plot a graph to show this relationship for the metals shown in Table 7.1. Write a sentence to summarise the relationship.

The Meissner effect

While investigating the effects of magnetic fields on superconductors, Walther Meissner discovered a striking phenomenon. When a superconducting material is placed in a magnetic field, it completely expels that field. No magnetic flux passes through the superconductor – see

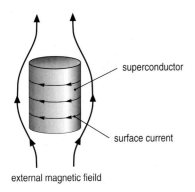

surface current

superconductor

external magnetic fieild

Fig 7.27 The surface current in the superconductor produces a magnetic field that expels the external field.

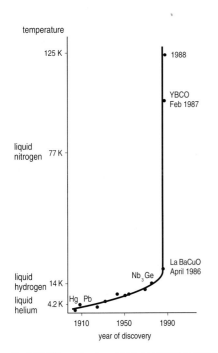

Fig 7.28 The Meissner effect: a magnet floats above a superconducting surface.

temperature

125 K — • 1988

YBCO
Feb 1987

liquid
nitrogen 77 K

La BaCuO
April 1986

liquid
hydrogen 14 K   Nb₃Ge

liquid
helium 4.2 K   Hg Pb

1910   1950   1990

year of discovery

Fig 7.30 After a slow increase over several decades, the discovery of new types of superconductor gave rise to a rapid increase in the achievable critical temperatures.

Fig 7.27. What happens is that currents flow in the surface of the superconductor, and these produce a magnetic field that exactly cancels out the external field.

(This is what happens in type-I superconductors. In type-II materials, the magnetic flux can penetrate in the form of thin tubes surrounded by circulating currents.)

The expulsion of a magnetic field by a superconductor is known as the Meissner effect. Fig 7.28 shows one consequence of this. A small magnet is placed above a dish of cold superconductor. The magnet is levitated – it floats above the superconductor as its magnetic field is expelled. There is a repulsive force between the magnet's field and the field due to the currents produced in the superconductor.

Fig 7.29 John Bardeen, who with Leon Cooper and John Schrieffer, won the Nobel Prize for Physics in 1972 with the BCS theory of superconductivity.

Explaining superconductivity

Onnes first observed superconductivity in mercury in 1911. However, it took nearly fifty years for a satisfactory theory to be devised that could explain the phenomenon. Bardeen, Cooper and Schrieffer proposed the 'BCS' theory in 1957, and they were eventually awarded the Nobel Prize for this work in 1972 (Fig 7.29).

The BCS theory suggests that electrons in a superconductor move as pairs, known as **Cooper pairs**. The electrons in a Cooper pair have opposite spins. When one electron is scattered by a vibration or an impurity in the metal, the other one is also scattered. If one electron *loses* energy when it is scattered, the other one *gains* an equal amount, because of its opposite spin. Overall, the pair has lost no energy, and so the current is unaffected.

Cooper pairs are formed most strongly at low temperatures; as the critical temperature T_c is approached, they tend to break up, and eventually superconductivity ceases.

The new superconductors

In 1986, the world of physics was shaken by the news that a new category of superconducting materials had been discovered. These were not even metals – they were ceramics, and they were superconducting at temperatures approaching 100 K. The first such materials were devised by Georg Bednorz and Alex Muller in Switzerland. The great attraction of high-T_c materials is that they do not rely on the availability of liquid helium. Rather, they will work in liquid nitrogen, which liquefies at 77 K. Nitrogen is readily available and cheap to liquefy.

Fig 7.30 shows how the best critical temperature attainable has increased during the 20th century. The material that Bednorz and Muller investigated

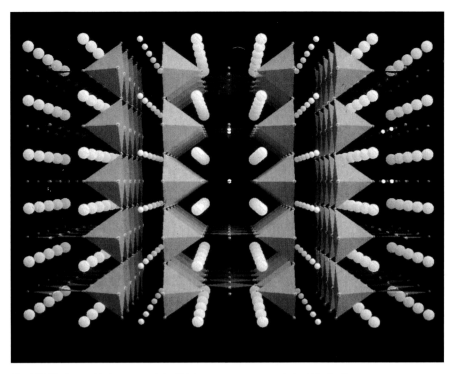

Fig 7.31 The 'perovskite' structure of the high-temperature superconductor $YBa_2Cu_3O_7$

was yttrium–barium–copper oxide, $YBa_2Cu_3O_7$, the structure of which is shown in Fig 7.31.

The availability of 'high-temperature' superconductors opens up the possibility of many more readily available devices. For example, a new generation of computers may use superconducting components. Since these would not generate heat as currents flow through them, they can be packed much more tightly together, increasing the computing power available in a given volume.

ASSIGNMENT

At the time of writing, superconducting materials have been found with critical temperatures above 130 K. Research continues at speed, and there is great commercial interest in the results.

Study current periodicals such as *New Scientist* and *Scientific American* to find out answers to these questions:

1. What are the most recently developed superconducting materials, and what are their critical temperatures?

2. What applications have been found for these 'high-temperature' superconductors?

SUMMARY

Electrical conduction in solids consists of the movement of charged particles: electrons, holes and ions. The conductivity of different types of materials – metals, semiconductors and insulators – depends on the availability of free charge carriers. The energy band theory is one way of representing this. Conduction in semiconductors can be controlled by doping with impurities. At low temperatures, some materials become superconducting – their resistance drops to zero.

Chapter **8**

DIELECTRIC PROPERTIES

If a conductor is placed in an electric field, the free charges in it move, and a current flows. An electrical insulator has no free charges, and so it cannot respond in the same way. Such a material is called a dielectric. Dielectrics are used by materials scientists not only to confine currents but also in the storage of charge (in capacitors) and the rapid and uniform generation of heat within poor thermal conductors. In this chapter you will see how dielectrics behave in static and alternating electric fields and how engineers make use of their properties.

LEARNING OBJECTIVES

After studying this chapter you should be able to:

1. describe the role of a dielectric material in a capacitor;

2. describe the three mechanisms that contribute to dielectric polarisation, and explain how they relate to the observed frequency dependence of electrical permittivity;

3. relate ferroelectricity and piezoelectricity to polarisation;

4. discuss the origin of dielectric loss;

5. give examples of situations where dielectric loss is a problem, and where it is made use of;

6. explain what is meant by dielectric breakdown;

7. define dielectric strength.

8.1 CAPACITORS

Capacitance and permittivity

A capacitor is a component used to store charge in an electric circuit. In principle, it consists of two parallel metal plates separated by a non-conducting gap. (This is shown in Fig 8.1.) When a capacitor is charged up to a potential difference V, it stores charge $+Q$ on one plate and charge $-Q$ on the other. The **capacitance** C is defined by

$$C = Q/V$$

For the capacitor shown in Fig 8.1, C depends on three factors: the area A of the plates, their separation d, and the material between the plates – known as the **dielectric**. To increase C, we need to increase A and decrease d. Hence we can write:

$$C = \varepsilon A/d$$

where ε is the **permittivity** of the dielectric. This is a measure of how easy it is for an electric field to pass through the material of the dielectric.

In practice, ε is often expressed as a multiple of ε_0, the **permittivity of free space** (a vacuum). This is because free space has the lowest possible

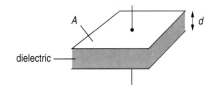

Fig 8.1 The construction of a parallel-plate capacitor.

permittivity; any insulating material placed between the plates of a capacitor is better than a vacuum. We write

$$\varepsilon = \varepsilon_r \varepsilon_0$$

where

$$\varepsilon_0 = 8.85 \times 10^{-12}\,\mathrm{F\,m^{-1}}$$

and ε_r is called the **relative permittivity** of the dielectric. Table 8.1 shows the relative permittivities of some dielectric materials.

QUESTIONS

Table 8.1 Values of relative permittivity ε_r

Dielectric material	Relative permittivity ε_r
vacuum	1.0000
air	1.0005
polyethene	2.3
nylon	4.0–4.5
glass	3.8–9.5
mica	7.0
water	80
barium titanate	1200

In these questions you will need the following value: $\varepsilon_0 = 8.85 \times 10^{-12}\,\mathrm{F\,m^{-1}}$. Values for ε_r are given in Table 8.1.

8.1 Calculate the permittivity of water and of barium titanate.

8.2 A parallel-plate capacitor is made of two plates each of area $1\,\mathrm{cm^2}$, separated by a polyethene sheet of thickness 0.05 mm. What is its capacitance? How much charge will it store if connected to a 100 V power supply?

8.3 It is desired to make a 100 μF capacitor using barium titanate as the dielectric. Suggest suitable dimensions for the plates and their separation.

8.4 Mica is a naturally occurring mineral with a structure of very thin sheets. Explain why this and its relative permittivity made it a suitable material for use as the dielectric in early capacitors.

Measuring permittivity

To measure the permittivity of a material such as polythene, a large capacitor is constructed, as shown in Fig 8.2, with a thin sheet of polythene as dielectric between two large metal plates. The capacitance of such an arrangement is small (perhaps $10^{-9}\,\mathrm{F}$), and so is quite difficult to measure. A simple technique uses a reed switch to charge and discharge the capacitor repeatedly through a sensitive ammeter – see Fig 8.3.

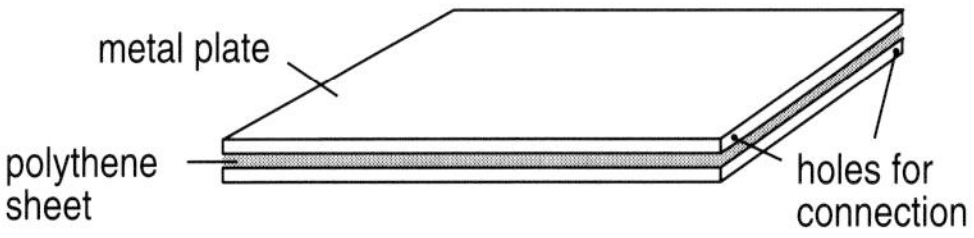

Fig 8.2 A capacitor for measuring the permittivity of polythene.

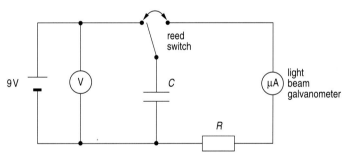

Fig 8.3 A circuit for measuring small capacitances.

A reed switch is a magnetic switch. It is positioned inside a small coil, which acts as an electromagnet. The coil is connected to a signal generator, so that the current through the coil reverses with frequency f. This makes the switch go back and forth with the same frequency, typically 100 Hz in this experiment.

When the switch is to the left, the capacitor C charges up to p.d. V. When the switch reverses to the right, the capacitor discharges through the light beam galvanometer, which is capable of reading currents of the order of a microamp.

Thus in 1 s, f pulses of charge, each of magnitude CV, pass through the meter. So the current I flowing through the meter (the charge that flows in 1 s) is given by

$$I = CVf$$

Hence by measuring V and I, and knowing the switching frequency f, we can deduce the capacitance C. (Notice that this equation is plausible: the current is greater for a larger capacitor, for a higher charging p.d., and if the capacitor is charged and discharged more frequently.) The permittivity of the dielectric can then be found from $C = \varepsilon A / d$.

QUESTIONS

8.5 A capacitor is charged up to a p.d. of 12 V and then discharged through a sensitive ammeter 200 times each second. The meter shows a current of 30 µA flowing. What is the capacitance of the capacitor?

8.6 A student carries out an experiment like that described above, to determine the relative permittivity of a plastic sheet. Her results are given below; use them to deduce the relative permittivity of the plastic.

current	$I = 40.0\,\mu A$
p.d.	$V = 10.0\,V$
frequency	$f = 120\,Hz$
area of plates	$A = 30\,cm \times 30cm$
thickness of plastic film	$d = 0.10\,mm$

8.7 In practice, the plastic sheet is unlikely to be perfectly flat and there is likely to be air as well as plastic between the plates in an experiment like this. Consequently, measuring the thickness of the plastic does not give an accurate measurement of the separation of the plates. How will this affect:

(a) the capacitance C;

(b) the current I?

Will the value of ε_r found from this experiment be too high, or too low, as a consequence?

8.2 DIELECTRIC ACTION

A dielectric, such as polystyrene or mica, placed in the space between two charged metal plates produces an increase of capacitance. If the plates carry a fixed charge, the potential difference between them must be reduced when the dielectric is inserted. We shall try to understand this by thinking about what is happening in the dielectric.

No long-range movement of charge can take place within the dielectric, as it can in a metal, but positive and negative charges within the particles of the material can be displaced slightly. Negative charges will be displaced in the direction of the positive plate and vice versa. As a result of the applied field, charges become aligned within the material. This process is known as **polarisation**. It causes charges that are of opposite sign to those on the plates to appear at the surface of the dielectric – Fig 8.4. Polarisation has the effect of reducing the p.d. between the plates, thereby increasing the capacitance.

There are three mechanisms that contribute to dielectric polarisation. They are illustrated diagrammatically in Fig 8.5, and are discussed briefly in the text.

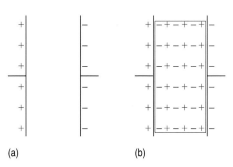

Fig 8.4 Dielectric polarisation: a parallel-plate capacitor **(a)** without dielectric and **(b)** with dielectric.

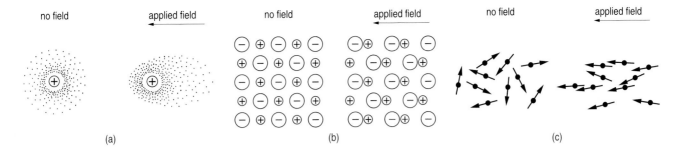

(a)   (b)   (c)

Fig 8.5 Schematic representation of the three mechanisms of polarisation induced by an electric field. **(a)** *Electronic:* the electron cloud around the nucleus distorts. **(b)** *Ionic:* positive and negative ions move in the field. **(c)** *Orientation:* molecular dipoles (represented by arrows) become partially aligned.

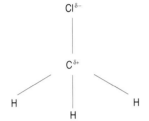

Fig 8.6 Charge distribution and electric dipole formation in the chloromethane molecule.

- Displacement of the electron cloud relative to the nucleus can occur in all particles and is known as **electronic polarisation**. For an electrically neutral atom, the centres of positive and negative charge no longer coincide, and this is said to be an induced electric dipole.

- Ions in a material with ionic bonding can also be displaced relative to one another in opposite directions. This is known as **ionic polarisation**.

- In some materials, covalent bonds are formed between atoms of different elements. One atom acquires more than a half-share of the pair of electrons of the bond and becomes slightly negative relative to the other atom. Such molecules are permanent dipoles and are said to be polar (see Chapter 1). Chloromethane is an example; the chlorine atom carries a small negative charge and the carbon atom a small positive charge – Fig 8.6. In the absence of an electric field, the dipoles are arranged randomly, but they become partially oriented in the presence of an electric field, making a further contribution to the total polarisation of the material. This is known as **orientation polarisation**.

All three types of polarisation contribute towards the permittivity of a dielectric; the relative contribution of each depends on the nature of the material. Table 8.2 shows some values of relative permittivity for various materials at low frequencies.

Table 8.2 Bonding and polarisation in a variety of materials

Material	Relative permittivity	Bonding	Polarisation
liquid hydrogen	1.2	non-polar covalent	electronic
polyethene	2.3	non-polar covalent	electronic
nylon-6,6	4.0–4.5	polar covalent	electronic + strong orientation
sodium chloride	5.6	ionic	electronic + ionic
chloromethane	12.6	polar covalent	electronic + strong orientation
barium titanate	1200	ionic	electronic + very strong ionic

Materials containing molecules that are permanent dipoles may have large values of permittivity because of a large contribution from orientation polarisation. Their permittivity, however, has a strong dependence on temperature because thermal agitation opposes alignment in an electric field. Increases of temperature tend to restore a random distribution of dipoles. Many polar molecules show a sudden change in the value of their permittivity at the melting point, when the molecules become free to rotate. Nitrobenzene is an example – Fig 8.7.

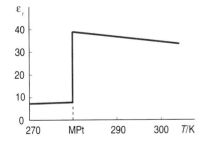

Fig 8.7 Variation of relative permittivity ε_r of nitrobenzene with temperature.

DIELECTRIC PROPERTIES

Frequency dependence of permittivity

If a dielectric material behaved in an ideal way, its dipoles would at all times follow any change in the applied field. Its polarisation would be instantaneous. In real materials, however, the particles are held together by attractive forces, which will resist reorientation. The rotation of dipoles is slowed down by this resistance and may not be in phase with a varying field.

Electronic polarisation occurs most rapidly because it is the result of the motion of low-inertia electrons. Ionic and orientation polarisation involve the motion of larger masses and there is greater resistance to the corresponding motion. If the dielectric is placed in an electric field alternating at low frequency, i.e. if slow a.c. is applied to the capacitor plates, all types of polarisation will follow the field variation. The permittivity will have its maximum value and will be identical with that measured under d.c. conditions. It is known as the **static permittivity** or sometimes the dielectric constant. As the frequency increases, a dipole may not be able to reorient during the period of oscillation of the field. The contribution from its polarisation to the permittivity will then cease. Since orientation polarisation is due to reorientation of comparatively large units, it stops contributing to the permittivity at a lower frequency than for the other forms. Ionic polarisation does not contribute beyond the infrared region, but electronic polarisation is present even at the frequencies of visible light. The total polarisability (and hence the permittivity) of a dielectric therefore decreases as the frequency of the alternating field increases. It decreases in a series of steps; each step corresponds to the cessation of a polarisation process as shown schematically in Fig 8.8(a). (The explanation of the different shapes of these steps is beyond the scope of this book.)

Fig 8.8 Variation of **(a)** total polarisation and **(b)** dielectric loss with frequency f of the applied alternating field. The peak values of dielectric loss occur at frequencies corresponding to large changes in polarisation.

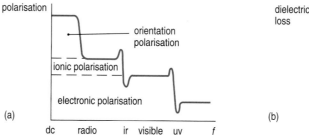

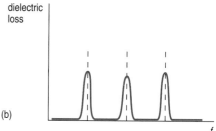

Dielectric loss

Energy is dissipated during dipole reorientation because the motion is opposed by frictional forces. Some of the electrical energy of the field is converted into heat in the dielectric material. This takes place in all materials to varying degrees and depends again on frequency and the polarisation process. The amount of energy dissipated depends on the size of the reorienting unit and the resistance to its motion; the effect is known as dielectric loss. The loss per cycle is greatest at frequencies corresponding to the steps of permittivity, and a series of loss peaks is observed, one for each polarisation process, as shown in Fig 8.8(b). Attempts are usually made to reduce energy dissipation through dielectric loss in electronic circuits by using appropriate dielectrics for the operating frequency range. However, the dielectric heating effect can be put to use in other applications. Domestic microwave ovens operate at a frequency of 2.4 GHz; at such a high frequency, losses are great for the water molecule. Rapid reorientation of the entire molecule against the resistance forces of its surroundings generates heat within any material containing water. Food is thus heated uniformly and rapidly but ceramic, paper or glass are not affected.

DIELECTRIC PROPERTIES

QUESTIONS

8.8 Copy Table 8.3 and complete the information given in it by deducing the nature of the bonding in the materials and which mechanisms contribute to the polarisation of the dielectric. (All the materials are insulators, except alumina, which conducts in the molten state.)

Table 8.3

Material		Relative permittivity	Bonding	Contributions to polarisation
poly(chloroethene) [a]		3.5		
sulphur	S_8	4.1		
quartz	SiO_2	4.5		
alumina	Al_2O_3	10		

[a] Poly(chloroethene) is also known as PVC

8.9 The permittivities of water and tetrachloromethane, CCl_4, measured at different frequencies are shown in Table 8.4. Explain these data in terms of polarisation mechanisms and their frequency dependence.

Table 8.4

Material		Relative permittivity	
		0 Hz	10^{14} Hz
water	H_2O	80	1.77
tetrachloromethane	CCl_4	2.24	2.13

8.10 Modern methods of making furniture use adhesives that require high temperatures to form joints between two pieces of wood. The adhesive-coated sections to be joined are placed between two metal electrodes connected to a radiofrequency generator operating in the MHz region. Explain how this produces heat within the joint and what advantages this method has over direct heating.

8.3 DIELECTRIC BREAKDOWN

If the p.d. across a capacitor is gradually increased, it stores more charge. However, eventually the dielectric suffers breakdown – that is, it ceases acting as a perfect insulator, and charge leaks through from one plate to the other. In the worst case, sparks may jump through from one plate to the other. The **dielectric strength** of the material has been exceeded.

Dielectric strength is an important material property that we need to know in order to design a capacitor. It is the p.d. per unit thickness of the dielectric at which breakdown occurs:

$$\text{dielectric strength} = (\text{p.d. at breakdown})/(\text{separation of plates})$$

$$= V_{\text{breakdown}}/d \qquad (\text{units: } V\,m^{-1})$$

There is no theory that enables dielectric strength to be calculated or predicted for a particular insulator, and its value may vary depending on the method of measurement. Manufacturers quote an 'operating voltage' for their capacitors. Below this value there should be no risk of dielectric breakdown, but it places a limit on the use of the capacitor.

Mechanisms of breakdown

Breakdown begins when free electrons or ions are released within the material. A number of causes may be responsible. Atomic bonds tend to be weaker at point defects or extended defects, making it easier for electrons to be removed. Impurity atoms may also donate electrons at lower field strengths than matrix atoms. The free electrons are accelerated by the field and collide with atoms. If they have sufficient kinetic energy, they may be able to remove the bound electrons from other atoms. An avalanche of electrons thus develops, and moves through the dielectric, with catastrophic results.

You might think that the dielectric strength of a material is independent of thickness. Very thin films, however, tend to break down at lower field strengths than expected because of defects such as pinholes or a region of crystalline material in an otherwise amorphous region making electron removal easier. If the material has interconnecting pores, these may provide channels along which breakdown occurs as a result of ionisation of gases within the pore. Power dissipation within the dielectric can also complicate matters because the consequent increase of temperature can further facilitate dielectric breakdown.

QUESTION

8.11 Table 8.5 lists the properties of some materials that could be used as the dielectric in a capacitor. The quantity $\tan \delta$ is a measure of the dielectric loss; the higher the value, the more power is dissipated in the capacitor during each cycle of alternating current.

For a parallel-plate arrangement of given dimensions, which material would result in a capacitor with

(a) the lowest 'operating voltage';

(b) the greatest capacitance;

(c) the greatest power dissipation for a particular operating voltage?

Table 8.5 Capacitor dielectric materials

Material	Relative permittivity	Dielectric loss factor ($\tan \delta$)	Dielectric strength/MV m^{-1}
PMMA [a]	3.25	0.04	1200
polyethene	2.3	0.0002	750
polystyrene	2.5	0.00015	700

[a] PMMA is the abbreviation for polymethylmethacrylate (perspex)

8.4 FERROELECTRIC MATERIALS

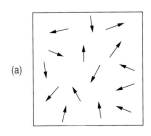

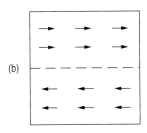

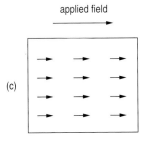

applied field

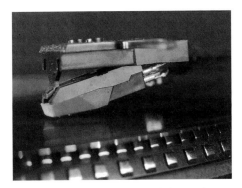

Fig 8.10 (a) In many dielectric materials, the molecular dipoles are randomly arranged in the absence of an electric field.
(b) In a ferroelectric material, the dipoles align spontaneously without an external field.
(c) In an applied field, there is even greater alignment. As a result, the material distorts.

Fig 8.11 The pick-up arm on a record player makes use of piezoelectric materials.

Many materials are made of molecules that are permanent dipoles – they have an uneven distribution of charge, so that one region of the molecule has a slight excess of positive charge, while another region has a corresponding negative charge (see Section 1.3 above). As already discussed, such a material will become polarised when placed in an electric field – for example, when used as the dielectric in a capacitor. This is shown in Fig 8.10(a).

Ferroelectric materials are a special category of dielectric material. They are polarised even when they are not in an electric field, as shown in Fig 8.10(b). The polar molecules align themselves within the material. This is known as **spontaneous polarisation**. If an electric field is applied, it has the effect of aligning the molecules more or less strongly.

Ferroelectrics have complicated crystal structures. One such material is lead zirconate titanate, with four different types of ion. Its structure is similar to that of the high-temperature superconductors discussed in Section 7.5 above. The crystal structure is such that positive and negative ions can move small distances relative to one another, giving rise to spontaneous polarisation.

Piezoelectricity

If an electric field is applied across a ferroelectric, it may become more polarised, as shown in Fig 8.10(c). You can see from the diagram that this results in a distortion of the material, greatly exaggerated in the illustration.

Similarly, if the material is squeezed, the polarisation changes. You will notice that opposite surfaces of the ferroelectric material have opposite charges. In other words, there is a p.d. across it. When the polarisation changes, the p.d. changes. Hence, squeezing the material produces a change in p.d. across it.

Thus we have two phenomena, which are mirror images of one another: apply a p.d. across the material and it deforms; deform the material and a voltage appears across it. Together, these are known as **piezoelectricity**.

Using ferroelectrics

Ferroelectric and piezoelectric materials have found a variety of uses (see Fig 8.11):

- Perhaps the most familiar use is in gas ignition systems, as used on gas fires and cookers. When the knob is pressed, a piezoelectric crystal is squeezed and the resulting p.d. produces a spark to light the gas.

- Because of their strong polarisation, ferroelectrics have a high relative permittivity. This makes them useful for making compact capacitors with high values of C. This is discussed further in the case study (Section 8.5).

- Record-player pick-ups may use a piezoelectric crystal to sense the movement of the stylus. Vibrations of the stylus are transmitted to the crystal, which experiences tiny changes in pressure. It responds by producing a correspondingly varying p.d.

- Loudspeakers and earphones can be made that operate in the reverse way. A sheet of ferroelectric polymer is subjected to a varying p.d. from an amplifier. Its deforms as the p.d. changes, and this sends vibrations out into the air. These are used in toys, novelty cards and badges.

- Ferroelectrics have also been put to use in intruder alarms and infrared imaging systems; some become opaque when a p.d. is applied across them, and this makes them useful for electrically operated shutters.

8.5 CASE STUDY: THE CHIP CAPACITOR

Background

Computers that were large enough to fill a room two decades ago have now been replaced by ones that sit on a desk-top. They also cost very much less. This is the result of a continuous drive to make smaller electronic components. You will be familiar with the integrated micro-circuit, or chip, which may have thousands of components built onto a small piece of semiconductor. If the size of electronic devices is to be reduced still further, then discrete components such as capacitors, inductors and resistors also have to be made smaller. In this case study we will see how new materials are designed and combined with new methods of manufacture to make small-volume, high-capacitance value capacitors.

Design parameters

Let us consider a parallel-plate capacitor having a capacitance C with plates of area A separated by a material of permittivity ε and thickness d. Designers define a parameter known as the 'volumetric efficiency' E_v of the capacitor. This is the capacitance per unit volume. A capacitor with a large capacitance and a small volume has a high volumetric efficiency. In this context the word 'efficiency' is being used to denote the efficient use of space. Now see how volumetric efficiency is related to the capacitor parameters by answering the following question.

1. (a) The volume of the capacitor in our case study is $A \times d$. Show that its volumetric efficiency is given by

$$E_v = \varepsilon / d^2$$

(b) Calculate the volumetric efficiency of an air-filled capacitor whose plates are separated by 5×10^{-4} m. (Permittivity of air = 9×10^{-12} F m^{-1}.)

From the equation above, we can draw some conclusions. The minimum possible value of d, the plate separation, depends on the required operating voltage and the dielectric strength. We are left with ε as a parameter that we can vary by design of the material.

The dielectric material

A family of ceramic materials based on barium titanate $BaTiO_3$ has been developed as capacitor dielectrics. They have a relative permittivity that can be as high as 10^4 and an acceptably low level of dielectric loss. These properties are a direct consequence of the crystal structure of the material.

Although these materials are called titanates, they have no discrete TiO_3 units comparable with CO_3 units in carbonates and NO_3 units in nitrates. They are made by mixing together two oxides of the general type AO and BO_2, where A and B are both metals. When heated at a high temperature, a reaction occurs in the solid to produce ABO_3. Possible elements for A and B are shown in Table 8.6.

The titanates have the unit-cell structure shown in Fig 8.12. Look carefully at the arrangement of the ions. You should be able to see that the barium and oxygen ions together form a 'face-centred cubic' arrangement similar to the cubic close-packed arrangement seen in Chapter 2. Barium ions are regularly arranged and occupy one-quarter of the total positions.

The titanium ions occupy octahedral sites. The coordination numbers of the ions are: barium, 12 (all oxygen); oxygen, 6 (two titanium and four barium); and titanium, 6 (all oxygen).

Dielectric polarisation of the titanates

Barium and oxygen ions differ slightly in size from one another and are considerably larger than the titanium ion. The hole at the centre of the

Table 8.6 Metals used in the barium titanate family of dielectric materials, ABO_3

Metal A		Metal B	
barium	Ba	titanium	Ti
strontium	Sr	zirconium	Zr
calcium	Ca	tin	Sn
lead	Pb		

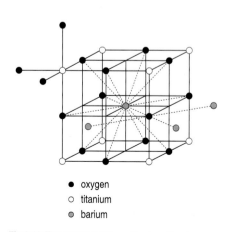

● oxygen
○ titanium
● barium

Fig 8.12 The crystal structure of barium titanate.

DIELECTRIC PROPERTIES

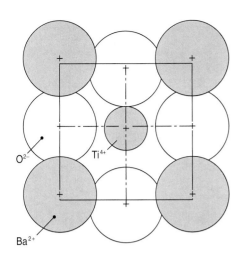

Fig 8.13 Tetragonal distortion along the *c* axis. Ion centres are marked +; the square marks the positions of ions in the undistorted cubic lattice. The titanium ion occupies one of two possible positions in the large octahedral hole.

oxygen-ion octahedron is wider than the diameter of the titanium ion. Consequently the titanium ion does not fit snugly into the octahedral hole – Fig 8.13. Both the position of the titanium ion in the octahedral hole and the crystal structure depend on temperature. Below ~130 °C the crystal structure is tetragonal. It is elongated slightly along the *c* axis, and there are two alternative positions of minimum energy for the titanium ion. It may be displaced above or below the centre of the octahedron by about 10^{-11} m. Fig 8.13 shows it in one of these positions.

In the tetragonal form, the unit cell no longer has a centre of symmetry as in the cubic form. Consequently the centres of positive and negative charge do not coincide. Each unit cell becomes a dipole, which has two orientations corresponding to the two positions of the titanium ion. Mutual interaction between neighbouring dipoles causes them to align in one of the preferred orientations. Regions in the crystal arise in which all dipoles are aligned in the same direction.

You should recognise that this spontaneous alignment of electric dipoles (spontaneous polarisation) means that these materials are ferroelectric. The prefix 'ferro' refers to the type of dipole alignment and is not associated with the presence of iron in these materials. Ferroelectricity and ferromagnetism describe the spontaneous alignment of electric and magnetic dipoles, respectively, in a preferred direction over a region known as a **domain**. (See Chapter 9 for a discussion of domains in magnetic materials.) Ferromagnetic behaviour was discovered before ferroelectric behaviour. The latter derives its name from being the electrical analogue of the former; ferroelectric materials are not ferromagnetic.

Fig 8.14 Microstructure of barium titanate ceramic. Ferroelectric domains can be seen within the grains.

Fig 8.14 shows the orientations of domains in grains of $BaTiO_3$. You can see that the domains are arranged randomly, so that the crystal as a whole has no net polarisation.

Each dipole contributes to the ionic polarisation of the material. As there are a large number of strong dipoles, the ionic polarisation and the permittivity are correspondingly large. If a ferroelectric crystal is placed in an electric field, the dipoles align in the field.

If the material is placed in an alternating polarising field, the domains will be forced to change their orientation every half-cycle. The polarisation follows a **hysteresis** cycle, which is analogous to that of a ferromagnetic material (see Chapter 9). Energy is required to reorient dipoles and to move domain walls. Hysteresis is therefore a source of energy loss, which can be associated with dielectric loss. Again, you will see the parallel with the dissipation of energy in the hysteresis cycle of rubber (see Section 4.4).

The temperature at which the spontaneous polarisation disappears, 130 °C for $BaTiO_3$, is known as the **Curie temperature**. At this temperature,

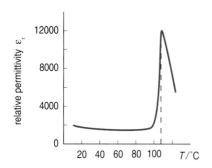

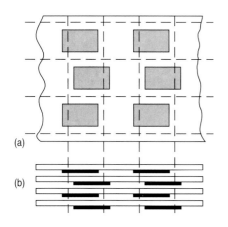

Fig 8.15 Variation of the relative permittivity of barium titanate with temperature.

(a)

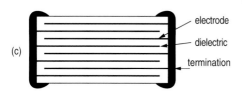

(b)

(c)

electrode

dielectric

termination

Fig 8.16 Fabrication of 'chip' capacitors.
(a) Electrode pattern printed onto a single layer of ceramic. (b) A sandwich of layers. (c) Silver electrode contacts in place.

there is sufficient thermal energy to prevent the titanium ion from adopting either of its preferred positions. The dipoles revert to a random distribution.

Fig 8.15 shows how the permittivity of $BaTiO_3$ varies with temperature. By mixing in other members of the titanate family, and by changing the grain size, it is possible to achieve values of relative permittivity ε_r up to 6000.

Fabrication

The volumetric efficiency of a capacitor can be improved by giving it a layered structure. A slurry of ceramic and polymer powder is spread to make a uniformly thin layer of dielectric. An electrode pattern is printed onto this layer using a fine suspension of the precious metals silver and palladium as an ink – Fig 8.16(a).

Similar layers are then stacked – Fig 8.16(b). The assembly is pressed to consolidate it into a sandwich of layers. It is then sliced along the dashed lines to give individual capacitor blocks or chips. It is fired to about 1350 °C to sinter the particles together. Silver paint is then applied to the block ends and fired at ~700 °C, to connect the precious-metal plates together – Fig 8.16(c).

2. Why do you think that a precious metal such as palladium, and not copper or aluminium, is used to fabricate the capacitor plates in our case study?

3. Explain why the multilayer arrangement is able to produce a higher value of capacitance than a single larger arrangement. Think about the interconnection of the plates.

4. A typical commercially available chip capacitor has 17 interleaved plates. It thus acts as 16 capacitors connected in parallel. The outer plates are separated by 5×10^{-4} m (the same separation as for the air-gap capacitor in question 8.12). The dielectric has a relative permittivity ε_r of 6000.

   (a) Calculate the separation of adjacent plates, d.

   (b) Calculate the volumetric efficiency of the capacitor.

   (c) Show that the volumetric efficiency of this capacitor is more than a million times greater than that of an air-gap capacitor occupying the same volume.

From question 4 above, we can see that we have increased the volumetric efficiency by a factor of more than one million. This has been achieved in two ways. By designing a multilayer construction, we have gained by a factor of 16^2; and by designing a material of very high dielectric permittivity, we have gained by a factor of 6000. This improvement in volumetric efficiency has been vital in efforts to miniaturise electronic circuitry.

SUMMARY

The space between the plates of a capacitor is filled with a material known as the dielectric. This material increases the capacitance because of its polarisation in an electric field – there is movement of charged particles, including polar molecules, ions and electrons. Materials that show spontaneous polarisation are known as ferroelectrics; their response to pressure is known as piezoelectricity.

By careful design of dielectrics, it is possible to enhance their relative permittivity, and to reduce the effects of dielectric loss and dielectric breakdown.

DIELECTRIC PROPERTIES

Chapter 9

MAGNETIC MATERIALS

Magnetic materials are essential for making magnets. They appear in loudspeakers and motors, as well as holding shopping lists to the fridge door. But there are many other uses of magnetic materials. Any electromagnetic device, such as a motor, dynamo or transformer, has magnetic circuits as well as electric circuits. Understanding the magnetic properties of materials has made it possible to increase greatly the efficiency of all of these devices.

> **LEARNING OBJECTIVES**
>
> After studying this chapter you should be able to:
>
> 1. define the relative permeability of a material;
>
> 2. distinguish between diamagnetic, paramagnetic and ferrromagnetic materials;
>
> 3. explain the terms 'saturation', 'hysteresis', 'remanence' and 'coercivity';
>
> 4. relate the terms 'hard magnetic material' and 'soft magnetic material' to their characteristic hysteresis behaviour;
>
> 5. explain the criteria for selection of magnetic materials for use in simple applications;
>
> 6. outline the domain theory of magnetism, and describe, in simple terms, how it may account for the observed magnetic behaviour of materials.

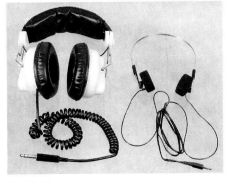

Fig 9.1 Stereo headphones

9.1 MAGNETISING AND DEMAGNETISING

Introduction

Let us start by thinking about a problem that may be solved by making a suitable choice of magnetic materials. Think about the design of a personal stereo system (a Walkman). It must be portable and lightweight. In designing suitable headphones, these requirements must be taken into account – Fig 9.1.

Headphones work on the same principle as loudspeakers. A varying current flows through a coil; the coil is in the field of a permanent magnet. It is the weight of the magnet that gives the principal contribution to the weight of the headphones.

QUESTION	
	9.1 Think about the magnets used in headphones. Should they be magnetically strong or weak? Permanent or easily demagnetised? Dense or less dense?

There are many different magnetic materials: some are strong, others weak; the magnetisation of some can be changed readily, that of others only with difficulty. In order to understand which material might be most appropriate for use in a particular situation, we must understand why

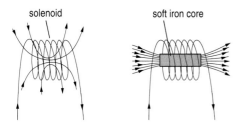

Fig 9.2 A core of ferromagnetic material inside a solenoid greatly increases the strength of the magnetic field.

materials have different magnetic properties. To understand these differences between materials, we must investigate the way in which a material becomes magnetised.

Magnetising a material

We are all familiar with iron as a magnetic material. Permanent magnets may be made from steel. Other metals such as nickel and cobalt are ferromagnetic; that is, like iron, they are strongly influenced by magnetic fields. Some ceramics, such as those based on barium ferrite, are also strongly magnetic. A familiar example is 'Magnadur'.

When a current flows in a solenoid, a magnetic field results. If a core of ferromagnetic material is placed inside the solenoid, the flux density is greatly increased. This is because the core has become magnetised, and contributes greatly to the flux density – see Fig 9.2.

The **relative permeability** μ_r of a material is defined by

$$\mu_r = B/B_0$$

where B is the flux density inside an infinitely long solenoid with the material present, and B_0 is the flux density with no material present. In principle, a toroidal (doughnut-shaped) solenoid should be used, as this is effectively endless. In practice, solenoids are used that have a length-to-radius ratio of at least ten.

The relative permeabilities of several materials are shown in Table 9.1. Notice that this property is very variable, and depends on the purity of the metal. It also depends on the flux density of the magnetising field. (Note that aluminium and copper are not ferromagnetic.)

The (absolute) **permeability** μ is the product of μ_r and the **permeability of free space**, μ_0:

$$\mu = \mu_r\mu_0$$

(Compare this with $\varepsilon = \varepsilon_r\varepsilon_0$.) In the SI system of units, the value of μ_0 is defined to be

$$\mu_0 = 4\pi \times 10^{-7}\,\mathrm{H\,m^{-1}}$$

Para-, dia- and ferromagnetism

You will notice in Table 9.1 that aluminium and copper have values of μ_r that are very close to 1. This means that they respond only very weakly to a magnetic field. A magnet will not pick up these metals.

For copper, μ_r is slightly less than 1. It is very weakly magnetic, and its magnetism opposes the external magnetic field. There is a very weak repulsion between copper and a permanent magnet; this can be measured using a very sensitive balance. A material like this, with μ_r less than 1, is said to be **diamagnetic**.

For aluminium, μ_r is slightly greater than 1. It is very weakly magnetic, and its magnetism is in the same direction as the external field. Any material with μ_r greater than 1 is said to be **paramagnetic**.

Diamagnetism and paramagnetism arise because of the way in which the atoms of the material respond to the external magnetic field. Every atom has a small degree of magnetism, arising from the spins of its electrons and its nucleus. When an external magnetic field is applied, these weak spins tend to line up in the field. In a diamagnetic material, they create an internal field that opposes the external field; in a paramagnetic material, they add to the external field.

The materials that we will be considering in the rest of this chapter are described as **ferromagnetic**. Iron is the most obvious example (hence *ferro*), but there are others, such as cobalt and nickel, and many alloys and compounds. A ferromagnetic material has a value of μ_r that is much greater

Table 9.1 Relative permeabilities of several materials

Material	μ_r
Fe (pure)	200 000
Fe (99% pure)	7 000
Ni (99% pure)	2 000
Mumetal [a]	100 000
Al	1.00002
Cu	0.99999
$MnZn(Fe_2O_4)_2$ (a ferrite)	2 500

[a] Mumetal is 16% Fe, 77% Ni, 5% Cu, 2% Cr

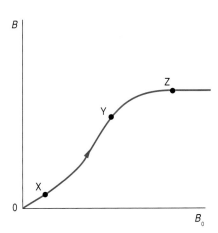

Fig 9.3 Initial magnetisation curve. The flux density B within a material depends on the flux density B_0 causing it.

than 1. Its atoms are strongly magnetic, and they are strongly aligned in an external field, so that the field within the material is much greater than the external field.

Initial magnetisation curve

When a ferromagnetic material, initially unmagnetised, is placed in an increasing magnetic field, the flux density within the material increases as shown in Fig 9.3. This is known as the 'initial magnetisation curve'. Note the following features of the graph:

- In the region OX the magnetisation is reversible.

- At any point, μ_r may be found from the graph by finding the ratio B/B_0.

- Y is the point at which μ_r has its greatest value.

- Beyond point Z, the material is fully magnetised – it has reached **saturation**.

Hard and soft materials

Permanent magnets are made from 'hard' magnetic materials; that is, considerable energy is required to change or reverse their magnetisation. 'Soft' magnetic materials can have their magnetisation changed more readily.

In the investigation that follows, you can see the effect of applying a rapidly varying magnetic field to a magnetic material. Hard and soft magnetic materials behave differently in alternating magnetic fields.

INVESTIGATION

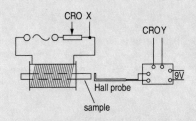

Fig 9.4 Circuit for observing magnetic hysteresis loops.

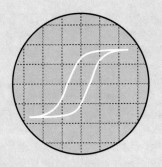

Fig 9.5 A typical hysteresis loop for a magnetic material.

Magnetic hysteresis

There are many situations where the magnetic field in a material changes cyclically. The core of a transformer is subject to such a varying field; you may be able to think of other examples. In this investigation, you can look at the way in which the magnetic flux density within a magnetic material depends on the applied field.

You will need some suitable rod-shaped samples of magnetic materials, e.g. soft iron, steel, mumetal, hacksaw blade, ferrite aerial core, nickel spatula.

Set up the circuit shown in Fig 9.4. The current in the coil produces a magnetic field B_0, which magnetises the sample. The Hall probe is used to detect the field B due to the sample.

The x deflection of the CRO is proportional to the current in the coil, and hence to B_0. The y deflection is proportional to B. Hence the CRO shows a display of how B depends on B_0.

With no sample present, the display is a straight line. The Hall probe is simply detecting the field in the coil. Adjust the rheostat to give a convenient x deflection.

Now place a suitable sample in the coil, with one end protruding a few centimetres, next to the Hall probe.

You will observe a hysteresis loop on the CRO, similar to Fig 9.5. The linear portions at the extreme high-field ends of the loop show that the magnetisation of the sample is saturated. (If you observe a simple ellipse, you must increase the current to the coil to produce saturation; it is easier to saturate small samples.)

Observe hysteresis loops for all your samples. Make a series of tracings of these loops using acetate sheet or tracing paper. Then answer the following questions:

1. Which materials give the largest and smallest area loops? (Hard

magnetic materials give large loops, soft materials give small loops.)

2. Which materials require the least magnetic field B_0 to produce saturation?

In practice, determination of the hysteresis behaviour and initial magnetisation curves of materials provides much important information for materials engineers. You may be able to design a circuit similar to Fig 9.4 with which you can observe the initial magnetisation curves of different materials, perhaps using a datalogger to collect the rapidly generated data.

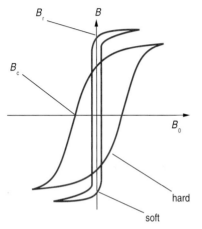

Fig 9.6 Magnetic hysteresis loops for hard and soft magnetic materials.

Magnetic hysteresis

The variation of the magnetic flux density B with applied flux B_0 is called a hysteresis loop. Fig 9.6 shows typical hysteresis loops for hard and soft magnetic materials.

When the applied magnetic field B_0 is reduced to zero, the material is still magnetised. This is known as **remanence**. On the graph, the remanent flux density is shown as B_r, which is the flux density that remains in the sample.

To demagnetise the sample (bring B to zero), a reverse field called the **coercive field** of flux density B_c must be applied. A hard magnetic material requires a greater coercive field to demagnetise it than a soft magnetic material.

The area of the hysteresis loop is related to the energy dissipated in the material during each cycle of magnetisation. The greater the area, the greater the energy that is dissipated.

QUESTIONS

9.2 On the same axes, sketch hysteresis curves for two magnetic materials, X and Y, with the following properties: both have the same remanent flux density; the coercive field of X is twice that of Y.

9.3 Would you expect a soft iron core or a hard steel core of identical

Uses of magnetic materials

As should now be clear, for lightweight stereo headphones, we require a strong, permanent and lightweight magnetic material. We would now say that it must be a hard magnetic material. Two such materials are given in Table 9.2.

Table 9.2

Material		B_c/T	B_r/T
samarium cobalt	$SmCo_5$	0.80	0.87
barium hexaferrite	$BaO \cdot 6Fe_2O_3$	0.24	0.38

The rare-earth alloy samarium cobalt has a very strong remanent flux density (200 000 times the Earth's magnetic flux density), and a very strong coercive field is required to demagnetise it. The values for barium hexaferrite are smaller, but this material is much cheaper, and in practice both are used in headphones. Samarium cobalt magnets are used in heart pacemakers, where cost is a less critical consideration.

MAGNETIC MATERIALS

9.2 DOMAIN THEORY

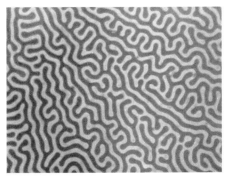

Fig 9.7 Magnetic domains in a garnet crystal. When viewed under polarised light, regions of opposite magnetisation show up as light and dark areas.

In order to understand why different magnetic materials behave differently, we must look at what is happening on the microscopic level. You are familiar with the way in which a loop of current produces a magnetic field. In a similar way, a ferromagnetic material is magnetic because of the circulating and spinning electrons within the atoms. Each electron may contribute to the magnetic flux within the material. Each atom behaves like a tiny magnet; we say it is a **magnetic dipole**.

In the investigation below you can see how these tiny magnets behave in a magnetic material. The magnetic dipoles of neighbouring atoms tend to be aligned, so that their contributions to the magnetic flux within the material add up. Regions where the magnetic dipoles are aligned in this way are called **domains** – see Fig 9.7. In the investigation you can observe magnetic domains in an initially unmagnetised garnet crystal, and see how they grow, shrink and move when you apply a magnetic field.

Cylindrical domains called 'bubbles' in thin garnet films form the basis of magnetic memories in some computers. In bubble logic, the presence of a bubble represents binary 0. Information may be stored at high density, as much as $10^7 \text{bits}/\text{cm}^2$.

INVESTIGATION

Observing magnetic domains
The concept of domains is fundamental to the modern theory of the magnetic behaviour of materials. There are several techniques that allow us to observe domains directly. In this experiment, you will look at the domains in a transparent garnet film. This is the material used for magnetic bubble memory stores in computers. You will observe their behaviour in a varying magnetic field.

How it works
The garnet is in the form of a thin transparent film, mounted horizontally. Place the apparatus on the microscope, and observe the garnet, illuminated from below (see Fig 9.8). You should be able to observe a pattern of dark and light areas – the domains.

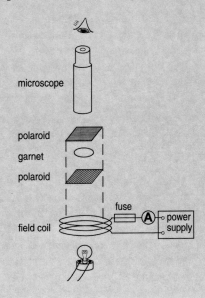

Fig 9.8 Exploded view of magnetic domains apparatus.

The garnet has two 'easy' directions of magnetisation, vertically upwards and vertically downwards. When viewed between suitably adjusted polaroids, which are built into the apparatus, the domains magnetised in one direction appear dark, the others appear light. (This is known as the Faraday effect.)

Varying the applied field

You have already made an important observation: with no external field, the material is already magnetised. There are equal areas of oppositely magnetised domains. There is no net magnetisation.

Observe the pattern of domains closely. How many domains are there altogether? (Approximately the same number as grooves on an LP.)

Now, observe the effect of applying an external magnetic field. Use a small permanent magnet. Remember the shape of the magnetic field near the pole of a magnet. The garnet will respond to a vertical field. Bring the magnet up to the garnet, and observe the change in the pattern of domains. What does the garnet look like when its magnetisation is saturated? Withdraw the magnet. Do the domains return exactly to their original pattern? Try reversing the magnet. Record all your observations.

You may be able to observe another effect. Use the magnet to saturate the magnetisation of the garnet. Then remove the magnet quickly. Observe the domain pattern for several seconds after this. You should see small abrupt changes in the domain pattern, after the external field has been removed. The domain walls move in a discontinuous way; this is called the Barkhausen effect.

Systematic variation of the applied field

The magnetic domains apparatus includes a built-in solenoid, which can be used to provide an external magnetic field. Connect up this solenoid to a d.c. power supply, with an ammeter and 1.25 A protective fuse in the circuit.

Slowly increase the current through the solenoid from zero to about 0.6 A. The magnetisation of the sample should be saturated at this stage. Reduce the current to zero. Is the sample demagnetised? Reverse the current, and repeat the experiment. You have cycled the external field from zero to a large positive value and back to a large negative value. You should be able to see signs of hysteresis. Record and explain your observations.

(To obtain more accurate results, the microscope may be adapted by incorporating a light-dependent resistor or photodiode to determine the intensity of light transmitted through the garnet. The results could then be collected using a datalogger.)

Finally, try replacing the power supply with a signal generator set at a low frequency, say 0.2 Hz. You should see the magnetisation of the sample varying cyclically. With large-amplitude variation of the applied field, you may observe sudden changes of magnetisation between the light and dark states. Try to explain these in terms of the hysteresis loop of a hard magnetic material.

Curie temperature

There is a magnetic interaction between neighbouring atoms that causes them to align. As you have seen, an external magnetic field causes the magnetic dipoles to align more strongly.

If the temperature of a ferromagnetic material is raised, the thermal motion of the atoms increases. This tends to disrupt the alignment of the magnetic dipoles. At a certain temperature, known as the **Curie temperature**, thermal agitation completely overcomes the magnetic alignment, and a ferromagnetic material becomes non-magnetic.

Domains and microstructure

In a soft magnetic material, the magnetisation is easily reversed. This is often the case in materials whose structures are cubic: they are relatively isotropic; and there are several directions in which it is easy to magnetise the material. Materials whose structures are hexagonal are often hard ferromagnets. They are easily magnetised along an axis at right angles to the close-packed planes, but much harder to magnetise in other directions. Thus it is difficult to force the atomic magnetic dipoles to reverse their direction.

Other ferromagnetic materials are hard for another reason. In the investigation, you saw how domain boundaries or 'walls' move through the material as its magnetisation changes. This movement is hindered by the presence of crystal defects – for example, small particles of iron carbide in steel cause domain-wall 'pinning'; the result is that soft iron may become a harder magnetic material on alloying.

In the case study (Section 9.3) you can read about the way in which silicon–iron transformer cores are designed to give low power losses by controlling the microstructure.

QUESTIONS

9.4 A piece of magnetised iron may be demagnetised by placing it in an alternating magnetic field, and gradually reducing the field to zero. Explain why this results in demagnetisation.

9.5 Some permanent magnets are made from many very small (1 mm diameter) particles, each of which consists of a single magnetic domain. Explain why such a magnet is very difficult to demagnetise.

9.6 Two magnetic memory devices have been used in computers: ferrite cores and magnetic bubble memories. Explain whether hard or soft magnetic materials would be suitable for these devices. What happens to the information stored if the power supply to the computer is switched off?

9.3 CASE STUDY: TRANSFORMER CORES

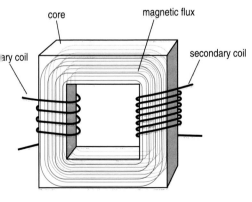

Fig 9.9 Construction of a transformer.

Background

One of the most important and extensive uses of magnetic materials is in the cores of transformers. You should already know the role played by transformers in a.c. supply, how they are constructed (see Fig 9.9), and the part played by the core in transformer action.

Many domestic appliances, such as stereo systems and televisions, contain transformers, which serve to change the voltage from 230 V to a more useful value. Similarly, many laboratory instruments such as power supplies and signal generators incorporate transformers.

1. Think about the role that the core plays in transformer action. Should it be made of a hard or a soft magnetic material?

Energy losses

If you have used a transformer, you may have noticed that it tends to get warm. Some transformers buzz and rattle. These are energy losses that we would like to avoid; the transformer is not 100% efficient.

Energy losses in transformers represent a serious cost to electricity producers, and great effort has been put in to improving their efficiency. An increase in efficiency from 98% to 99% could save the cost of adding one power station to the generating capacity of the UK electricity supply industry. Let us look at the origin of these losses, and how they may be reduced.

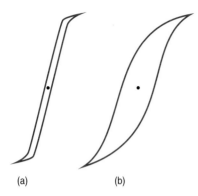

(a)   (b)

Fig 9.10 Hysteresis loops for two magnetic materials.

Hysteresis losses

The magnetic flux density in a transformer core reverses many times a second. The hysteresis loop shows how the flux B in a material lags behind the flux B_0 producing it. The smaller the area of the hysteresis loop, the better the material is at transmitting magnetic energy without losses.

Another important consideration is the question of saturation. It is important that the magnetisation should not saturate, as this limits the energy that is transmitted.

2. Fig 9.10 shows the hysteresis loops of two magnetic materials available for use in transformer cores. Which is more suitable?

3. Table 9.3 shows the saturation flux density for several magnetic materials. Why are metals preferred to ceramics for the cores of mains transformers?

Table 9.3 Properties of four magnetic materials: the first two are metal alloys; the others are ferrite ceramics

Material	Saturation flux density /T	Resistivity /Ω m
Fe (1% C) steel	2.00	2.0×10^{-7}
Fe (3% Si)	1.98	4.8×10^{-7}
MnZn(Fe$_2$O$_4$)$_2$	0.34	0.2
NiZn(Fe$_2$O$_4$)$_2$	0.37	1000

Movement of domain walls

As the magnetisation of the core changes, the domains within the core change. Domain walls move, in the way that you saw in the investigation. Energy is needed for the domain walls to move past obstacles such as point defects and dislocations, and to reverse the direction of magnetisation.

You will recall that, within a crystalline magnetic material, there are 'easy' directions of magnetisation. Fig 9.11 shows the results of an experiment to find the easy directions of magnetisation of a crystal of an iron–3% silicon alloy. Within the crystal the easy direction of magnetisation is along the cube edge. Only a small flux density is required to saturate the magnetisation in this direction.

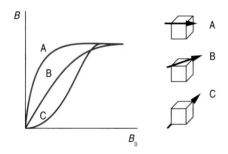

Fig 9.11 Initial magnetisation curves for Fe–3% Si alloy, in three different crystal orientations. A = cube edge, B = face diagonal, C = body diagonal.

How can we use this knowledge? It is impracticable to use single crystals, but it is possible to produce an Fe–3% Si alloy in which the grains are preferentially oriented.

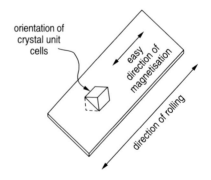

Fig 9.12 Orientation of crystal planes in rolled Fe–3% Si alloy.

The alloy is rolled out into flat sheets and subsequently annealed. Fig 9.12 shows how the grains are oriented so that the easy direction of magnetisation lies along the direction of the magnetic flux within the core.

Annealing removes imperfections (which result from rolling) in this structure. Fig 9.13 shows the effect of annealing on the hysteresis loop.

The process of cold rolling and annealing results in a microstructure that allows the magnetisation to be easily reversed, with minimum hysteresis losses. This is an example of a material whose microstructure has been designed to give improved magnetic properties.

4. Look at Fig 9.13. What does it tell you about the effect of annealing on hysteresis losses in Fe–3% Si?

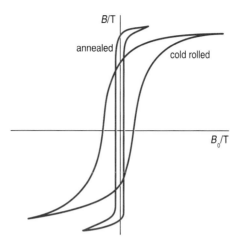

Fig 9.13 Effect of annealing on the hysteresis loop of cold-rolled Fe–3% Si alloy.

Eddy current losses

The other source of power loss in a transformer core arises from eddy currents that flow in the core, giving rise to heating. The core is a stationary conductor in a changing magnetic flux density, B. An e.m.f. is induced, which causes currents to flow, producing a flux density in opposition to B. Lamination, in which the core is made of thin sheets, reduces the cross-sectional area, and hence the e.m.f. induced in each lamina is reduced.

Transformers are not only used in the mains electricity supply; they have uses at higher frequencies too. Eddy current losses become very significant at high frequencies, particularly microwave frequencies.

5. Explain, using Faraday's law, e.m.f. $= -d\Phi/dt$, why eddy currents are a greater problem at microwave frequencies than at mains frequencies. Use the information in Table 9.3 to explain why ceramic cores are used in transformers for high-frequency applications.

Saving power

The development of materials with controlled microstructures, such as the Fe–3% Si alloy with grains preferentially aligned, has led to a dramatic reduction in power losses in transformers. Fig 9.14 shows how core losses in commercial transformers have been reduced during the 20th century. New developments include the use of metallic glasses (see Chapter 2), materials that are equally easy to magnetise in all directions, and which present little opposition to domain-wall movement.

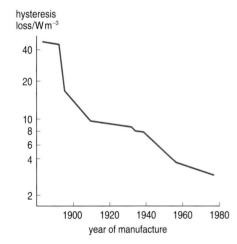

Fig 9.14 Reduction in core loss of commercial transformer material.

SUMMARY

Magnetic materials may be divided into hard and soft types. A hard magnetic material shows high remanence, and a high coercive field is required to demagnetise it. The hysteresis loop shows how the flux density within a material varies as the external field is changed. Domain theory explains the behaviour of magnetic materials in terms of the alignment of neighbouring atomic dipoles.

Chapter 10

REFRACTIVE INDEX

Light is a form of electromagnetic radiation. It has electrical and magnetic characteristics, and consequently interacts with any material through which it passes. This interaction depends on the electrical and magnetic properties of the material.

LEARNING OBJECTIVES

After studying this chapter you should be able to:

1. state and use Maxwell's equation, $c = (\mu\varepsilon)^{-\frac{1}{2}}$;

2. deduce the expression for the refractive index of a material, $n = (\mu_r\varepsilon_r)^{\frac{1}{2}}$;

3. relate measured values of refractive index and relative permittivity.

10.1 ELECTROMAGNETIC WAVES

Introduction

The refractive index is an important property of a material that depends on both its dielectric and magnetic properties. Let us start by recalling the meaning of the **refractive index**, n, of a material:

$$n = (\text{speed of light in vacuum})/(\text{speed of light in material})$$

(This result follows from the definition of n.)

Since the speed of visible light is greatest in a vacuum, it follows that, for all materials, $n > 1$.

Light as an electromagnetic wave

You will know that light is an electromagnetic wave, part of the electromagnetic spectrum. That is, it is a transverse wave having electric and magnetic field components perpendicular to each other and to its direction of propagation. This is represented in Fig 10.1.

When light enters a medium, these electric and magnetic field components interact with electric charges and magnetic dipoles within the material. The interaction is strongest in materials with high electrical permittivity ε and high magnetic permeability μ. Thus it is not surprising to find that the speed of light in a material depends on both ε and μ.

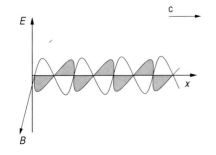

Fig 10.1 An electromagnetic wave such as light consists of alternating electric E and magnetic B field components, moving with velocity c. E, B and c are mutually perpendicular.

Maxwell's equation

Maxwell was the first scientist to deduce relationships that successfully connected light, electricity and magnetism. He was able to show that the speed of light, c_m, in a medium is given by:

$$c_m = (\mu\varepsilon)^{-\frac{1}{2}} \tag{10.1}$$

For a vacuum, we have:

$$c = (\mu_0\varepsilon_0)^{-\frac{1}{2}} \tag{10.2}$$

10.1 In the SI system of units, the speed of light c and the permeability of free space μ_0 have defined (fixed) values:

$$c = 299\,792\,458 \text{ m s}^{-1}$$

$$\mu_0 = 4\pi \times 10^{-7} \text{ H m}^{-1}$$

Use these values to deduce the value of the permittivity of free space ε_0 to as many significant figures as you can.

10.2 REFRACTIVE INDEX

From equations (10.1) and (10.2) we can deduce a relationship between n, ε_r and μ_r. Since $\mu = \mu_r\mu_0$ and $\varepsilon = \varepsilon_r\varepsilon_0$, we can rewrite equation (10.1) in the form:

$$c_m = (\mu_r\mu_0\varepsilon_r\varepsilon_0)^{-\frac{1}{2}} \tag{10.3}$$

and, referring to the definition of refractive index, dividing equation (10.2) by equation (10.3) gives

$$n = c/c_m = (\mu_r\varepsilon_r)^{\frac{1}{2}} \tag{10.4}$$

This is the very simple relationship that Maxwell deduced between n, μ_r and ε_r. For most transparent materials, $\mu_r = 1$, so that $n \approx \varepsilon_r^{\frac{1}{2}}$. Also, since for all materials, $\varepsilon_r > 1$, it follows that $n > 1$.

For many materials, good agreement is found between the values of n and $\varepsilon_r^{\frac{1}{2}}$. In others, agreement is less good. This arises because, at optical frequencies (of the order of 10^{14} Hz), only electronic polarisation contributes to n.

QUESTIONS

10.2 Look at Table 10.1, which compares measured values of n and ε_r. For which materials is there good agreement between values of n and $\varepsilon_r^{\frac{1}{2}}$? Why might there be bad agreement in the other cases? (It may help you to think back to the discussion of relative permittivity and how this depends on frequency in Section 8.2 above.)

10.3 The low-frequency permittivity and square of the refractive index for a number of materials are shown in Table 10.2. Explain these data in terms of mechanisms of polarisation.

Table 10.1 Relative permittivity and refractive index for some transparent materials

Material	ε_r	$\varepsilon_r^{\frac{1}{2}}$	n
diamond (C)	5.68	2.38	2.38
polyethene	2.30	1.52	1.51
paraffin	2.20	1.48	1.48
quartz (SiO$_2$)	3.85	1.96	1.46
soda glass	7.60	2.76	1.52

Table 10.2

Material		(Refractive index)^2	Relative permittivity
liquid hydrogen	H$_2$	1.23	1.23
sodium chloride	NaCl	2.25	5.6
methanol	CH$_3$OH	1.764	33.0

SUMMARY

Light is a form of electromagnetic radiation that has both electrical and magnetic interactions with materials. The refractive index of a material thus depends on both its relative permittivity and its relative permeability: $n = (\mu_r\varepsilon_r)^{\frac{1}{2}}$. For free space, the speed of light is given by Maxwell's relationship: $c = (\mu_0\varepsilon_0)^{-\frac{1}{2}}$.

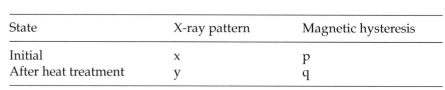

EXAMINATION QUESTIONS:
Theme 3

T3.1

The X-ray diffraction pattern and magnetic hysteresis behaviour of a sample of a metallic alloy were determined before and after heat treatment, as detailed in the table, and are shown in the figures.

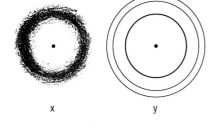

x   y

State	X-ray pattern	Magnetic hysteresis
Initial	x	p
After heat treatment	y	q

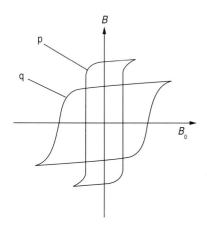

(a) Define the terms *remanence* and *coercivity* and state

　(i)　whether the larger remanence occurs before or after heat treatment,

　(ii)　whether the larger coercivity occurs before or after heat treatment.

　Discuss whether the sample could be described as magnetically *hard* in either its initial state or final state.

(b) Describe the structure of the sample in its initial state and explain why the magnetic properties observed are as shown in curve p.

(c) Explain what happened to the microscopic structure during the heat treatment of the metallic alloy. Why does this affect the magnetic properties of the alloy in the way shown?

(NEAB 1989)

T3.2

(a) When a beam of light travels from air into a transparent material the beam is refracted at the interface between the two media.

　(i)　Explain what is meant by *refraction*.

　(ii)　Define the refractive index of a material in terms of the speed of light.

　(iii)　The refractive index of a material depends on both magnetic and electric properties of the material. Defining the symbols you use, show that the refractive index of a material is given by the expression

$$n = (\mu_r \varepsilon_r)^{\frac{1}{2}}$$

The relative permittivities of the plastics, polystyrene and acrylic, at low frequencies are observed to be 2.5 and 3.4 respectively. The refractive indices of the materials, measured using an optical (high frequency) method, are observed to be 1.59 for polystyrene and 1.49 for acrylic.

　(iv)　The relative permittivity of polystyrene does not change significantly with increasing frequency up to optical frequencies. By referring to the relationship given in part (iii), calculate the value of the relative permeability of polystyrene at optical frequencies.

　(v)　The relative permeability of acrylic is similar to that of polystyrene at optical frequencies. Calculate the value of the relative permittivity of acrylic at optical frequencies and explain the difference in its value when compared with that quoted for low frequencies.

(b) An LED emits light of a particular colour when it is forward biased. Different semiconductor materials may be used to produce light of different colours.

    (i) Sketch and label the energy band diagram for a typical intrinsic semiconductor.

    (ii) By referring to your diagram, explain why the colour of the light emitted by an LED will depend upon the particular semiconductor used.

(NEAB 1994)

T3.3

(a) (i) Name *three* types of polarisation that contribute towards the permittivity of a dielectric.

    (ii) There is an increase in capacitance when a dielectric is placed between the plates of a capacitor without a change in either the distance between the plates or the area of plates. Describe, in terms of one of the mechanisms referred to in (i), why this is so.

(b) The diagram shows the structure of a particular type of capacitor.

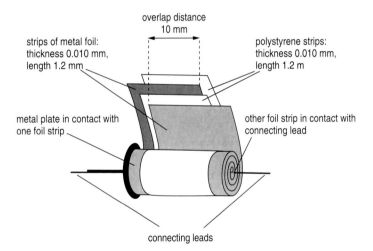

Two long strips of metal foil have sandwiched between them two strips of polystyrene. Such capacitors can operate up to frequencies of the order of a few GHz without a significant decrease in capacitance.

    (i) Name the type or types of polarisation that make polystyrene a suitable choice of dielectric for the capacitor shown above, making your reasoning clear.

    (ii) By using the dimensions shown in the diagram and any other information as necessary from data in a data book, determine the capacitance of the capacitor shown.

    (iii) Explain why there will be a maximum operating voltage for such a capacitor. Using values taken from data in a data book, determine the maximum operating voltage for the capacitor shown above.

(NEAB 1994)

T3.4

(a) State *one* piece of experimental evidence to suggest that the electrons of an isolated atom can have only certain discrete energies. Describe briefly how this evidence may be used to determine the differences in the possible energies of the electrons.

(b) Use a diagram to show how the energy levels of atoms are affected when many similar atoms come together to form a solid.

(c) (i) Draw energy level diagrams for an *insulator* and a *metal*.

    (ii) Explain why metals are opaque to light.

    (iii) Why is it reasonable to assume from the energy level diagram that insulators are transparent? Explain why, in fact, many insulators are opaque.

(d) A single crystal of a certain insulating material is found to be transparent to light of wavelength greater than 500 nm (blue/green).

    (i) Calculate the value for the energy band gap.

    (ii) State the colour of the transmitted light when the crystal is illuminated with white light.

(NEAB 1992)

T3.5

(a) Explain the meaning of the following terms in relation to the construction of practical capacitors.

    (i) relative permittivity

    (ii) dielectric strength

    (iii) dielectric breakdown

    (iv) dielectric loss

(b) It is proposed to use parallel plate capacitors for energy storage. Derive an expression for the maximum energy which can be stored in unit volume of a material, taking into account the possibility of dielectric breakdown.

(c) Choose a dielectric material from the list to store the maximum energy per unit volume, justifying your choice with suitable calculations.

Material	Relative permittivity	Density /kg m^{-3}	Dielectric strength /kV mm^{-1}
PET	2.9	1400	42
PMMA	3.2	1200	16
PE	2.3	950	19
Glass	7.6	2500	15
Mica	8.7	2800	80

(d) Suggest a situation when it may be more appropriate to consider the energy per unit mass. Calculate the maximum energy which could be stored in unit mass of a capacitor working at a potential difference of 500 V using the most suitable material from the above list. (Neglect the mass and volume of the electrodes.)

(NEAB 1988)

Appendix A

ANSWERS TO QUESTIONS AND CASE STUDIES

Chapter 1

1.1   Silver
1.2   Cost
1.3   Lower thermal conductivity
1.4   Malleability
1.5   Lighter
1.6   **(a)** Repulsive greater for small r **(b)** Attract when far apart
1.7   **(a)** 0.33 nm approx   **(b)** 0.42 nm approx
1.8   **(a)** Magnets attract, springs repel, hence equilibrium (or oscillations)
        (b) As for two neutral atoms
        (c) As for two neutral atoms
        (d) Attractive and repulsive forces are acting.
1.9   **(a)** 0.34 nm approx
        (b) 0.9×10^{-13} J approx
1.11 **(a)** True   **(b)** False   **(c)** True   **(d)** False   **(e)** True
1.12 **(a)** A; shallower potential well   **(b)** A; wider potential well
1.13 Two
1.15 One, one, four
1.17 HCl has permanent dipoles, H_2 has only instantaneous dipoles.
1.18 **(a)** C   **(b)** D   **(c)** A   **(d)** B   **(e)** A

Chapter 2

2.2   Visible light: 400–700 nm; X-rays: 10 nm–1 pm
2.3   Typically 0.1–0.2 nm
2.4   Wavelength comparable to spacing of atoms
2.5   Can study small (regions of) specimens
2.8   Crystal: regular array of dots, reflecting regular crystalline ordering.
        Powder: rings, showing presence of all possible orientations of crystal planes.
        Liquid: diffuse rings, showing relative disorder of molecular arrangement.
        Glass: similar to liquid.
2.9   Hcp and ccp (of course)
2.10 Six; twelve
2.11 Disorderly packing; amorphous material
2.12 As T increases, particles vibrate with greater amplitude. Since the force–separation curve is not symmetrical, their average separation increases. Also, the concentration of vacancies increases with increasing T. Hence the volume of the solid increases.
2.13 **(a)** False   **(b)** False   **(c)** True
2.14 **(a)** False   **(b)** True   **(c)** False

Chapter 3

3.2   Contraction on solidifying
3.3   **(a)** Not always true. When the (directional) bonds within ice break up, the molecules can pack more closely in the resulting liquid.

(b) Not strictly true. In a solid, particles diffuse from one point to another at temperatures above approximately $T_m/2$. In a liquid, the particles are not completely free to move. There is some local ordering.

3.4   **(a)** Different   **(b)** Different   **(c)** Different

Chapter 4

4.1   **(a)** Upper   **(b)** Lower   **(c)** Upper
4.2   **(a)** Tension breaks mortar   **(b)** Compression where stones in contact
4.3   **(a)** 0.01%   **(b)** 100 MPa   **(c)** 200 GPa
4.4   **(a)** Iron, steel   **(b)** Lead
      (c) Both arise from force between iron atoms.
4.5   0.98 mm
4.6   **(a)** 600 MPa   **(b)** 30 MPa
4.7   **(a)** D   **(b)** E   **(c)** D   **(d)** B
4.8   **(a)** Wood, glass, copper, biscuit, brick
      (b) Wood, glass, biscuit, brick
      (c) Plasticine, biscuit, polyethene
      (d) Biscuit   **(e)** Plasticine, polyethene, copper
      You may not agree with all these answers; they depend on personal judgement. You should be able to justify your answers.
4.9   **(a)** Difficult to stretch, breaks easily
      (b) Stretches a good deal, will not break
      (c) Difficult to stretch and to break
      (d) Pulls apart very easily, with some stretching
4.10 Low creep, because high melting point, but they are brittle.
4.11 **(a)** 300 MPa
4.12 **(a)** 2.4 J   **(b)** 1.5 J   **(c)** 0.9 J

Case study
1   CFRP
2   Wood
3   Cheaper
4   Expensive
5   Wood rots and is attacked by biological organisms.
6   Wood and concrete are comparably cheap – see table:

Material	$(\rho^2/E)^{1/2} \times P$
steel	3.5
concrete	1.6
CFRP	261
wood	1.1

Chapter 5

5.1   Cannot have slip, so no plastic deformation
5.2   **(a)** A bit lower   **(b)** Lower   **(c)** Much greater
5.3   Tape is strong along its length (covalent bonds), but weak perpendicularly (van der Waals bonds).
5.4   Bottle has less parallel alignment of molecules.
5.6   Ceramics and plastics are less dense than metals, the engine is lighter and so less fuel is used in moving around. (Also ceramics survive higher temperatures, so engines can be more efficient.)

5.9　'Plastics' below T_g show glassy, non-plastic behaviour.
5.10　**(a)** Diamond　**(b)**　Steel　**(c)** Glass
5.12　**(a)** True　**(b)** True　**(c)** False
5.13　**(a)** True　**(b)** False　**(c)** True
5.14　**(a)** True　**(b)** True　**(c)** False

Case study

1　Need high pressure and temperature for high efficiency.
2　**(a–d)** Need high values　**(e)** Need low density
3　Ceramics are brittle. If a ceramic breaks, it is sudden and would probably cause serious damage. Metals are plastic and deform gradually, giving advanced warning of failure.

Chapter 6

6.1　Transparent, stiff, strong
6.2　Coloration visible (caused by impurities)
6.3　Bubbles, variations in thickness, impurities, crystallisation
6.5　Silica glass 9.94×10^{-19} J
　　Borosilicate glass 6.63×10^{-19} J
　　Soda-lime glass 5.68×10^{-19} J
　　Greatest photon energy approximately E_g
6.6　Porcelain has a fine grain structure. Light is scattered at grain boundaries. Many insulators appear white for this reason.
6.7　Shortest wavelength of photon transmitted is approximately 565 nm. Green, blue and violet light is absorbed. The result is that sulphur appears yellow.
6.8　**(a)** Yes　**(b)** No

Case study

2　Ray 2 travels further, so arrives later.
3　**(b)** 2.14×10^8 m s^{-1}; 280 million reflections
　　(d) 4.6 µs
4　Non-uniform density; cracks, impurities, etc.
5　Copper; iron
6　Silica absorption
7　Rayleigh scattering
8　Hydroxyl ion absorption at 1400 nm
9　1550 nm; 70 km
10　100 km

Chapter 7

7.2　**(a)** 10^{-15} S m^{-1}　**(b)** 10^8 S m^{-1}
7.3　**(a)** 18.8 S　**(b)** 0.053 Ω
7.4　0.21 m s^{-1}
7.5　1.0×10^{22} m^{-3}
7.6　Electron in VB 'captures' photon, moves up to CB, and so can move freely.
7.7　**(a)** Broad absorption band due to alumina
　　(b) Narrow yellow and blue absorption due to Cr ions
　　(c) Yellow and blue absorbed, so red transmitted
7.8　Mobile electrons absorb visible light.
7.9　Graphite has planes over which electrons move. Polyethyne has linear molecules.

7.10 The energy gap is small, so that all wavelengths of visible light are absorbed. However, at room temperature, few electrons are in the conduction band, so resistivity is high.

7.12 **(a)** The value of n increases.
(b) Conduction electrons flow from hot end (high concentration) to cool end.
(c) The n-type material will behave as an intrinsic semiconductor; p-type will show current in opposite direction, since the current will largely consist of holes.

7.13 **(a)** 0.016 V **(b)** Voltage would be 10^7 times smaller.

7.17 High-T_c materials have high B_c.

Chapter 8

8.1 Water, $7.1 \times 10^{-10}\,F\,m^{-1}$
Barium titanate, $1.1 \times 10^{-1}\,F\,m^{-1}$

8.2 40 pF; 4000 pC

8.3 $100\,cm^2$, 0.01 mm (for example)

8.5 $1.25 \times 10^{-8}\,F$

8.6 4.2

8.7 **(a)** C is smaller than calculated.
(b) I is smaller than expected, so ε_r is smaller.

8.8 See completed table below:

Material		Relative permittivity	Bonding	Contributions to polarisation
poly(chloroethene)		3.5	polar covalent	electronic + weak orientation
sulphur	S_8	4.1	non-polar covalent	electronic
quartz	SiO_2	4.5	polar covalent	electronic + orientation
alumina	Al_2O_3	10	ionic	electronic + ionic

8.9 Water has a large low-frequency orientation polarisation contribution to its permittivity. Only electronic polarisation is present at high frequencies. Tetrachloromethane is non-polar and has no orientation polarisation contribution. Its permittivity thus changes little with frequency.

8.10 Dielectric loss mechanisms generate heat within the joint. The process is quicker and more efficient in terms of energy usage.

8.11 **(a)** Polystyrene **(b,c)** PMMA

Case study

1   **(b)** $3.6 \times 10^{-5}\,F\,m^{-3}$

2   Palladium survives high-temperature sintering, and does not oxidise.

3   Multilayer construction = many capacitors with plates very close together.

4   **(a)** 31 μm **(b)** $55.3\,F\,m^{-3}$
(c) 1.5 million times greater

Chapter 9

9.1 Strong, permanent, low density

9.3 Hard gets warmer

9.5 Domain walls cannot move past grain boundaries. The magnetisation of a single grain must reverse instantaneously and completely, an unlikely event.

9.6 Hard magnetic materials are used, so that the information stored does not deteriorate, and is not lost when the power supply is switched off.

Case study

1 Soft

2 Material (a); smaller loop means smaller losses during each cycle.

3 Can reach higher fields without saturating, so can transmit more power.

4 Smaller losses after annealing

5 Higher frequency means higher losses; ceramics give lower losses each cycle, but cannot transmit so much power.

Chapter 10

10.1 $8.85418 \times 10^{-10} \, \mathrm{F \, m^{-1}}$

10.2 Good agreement for first three. For others, the problem is that n is measured at optical frequencies ($10^{14} \, \mathrm{Hz}$) where only electronic polarisation is significant, but ε_r is measured at low frequencies where ionic and orientation polarisation are important.

10.3 Liquid hydrogen: good agreement between n_2 and ε_r. Electronic contribution to permittivity is dominant.

Sodium chloride: ionic contribution to permittivity is significant at low frequency.

Methanol: orientation contribution to permittivity is significant at low frequency.

Appendix B

CAREERS IN MATERIALS SCIENCE AND ENGINEERING

A WIDE RANGE OF OPPORTUNITIES

Materials, which are the focus of this part of the A-level physics course, are important to all manufactured goods. Improvements in materials can make the difference between success and failure for a new product. This has been recognised by the Government, who are trying to increase the rate at which UK manufacturers incorporate new or improved materials into their products. There is, therefore, a wide range of career opportunities open to those who study materials science and engineering.

Producers, fabricators and users of materials are found in a range of industries, including construction, transport, energy supply, domestic appliances, sports goods, packaging, medical supplies and farm machinery. In these diverse industrial areas, there are opportunities in research and development, production management, materials selection and technical sales or marketing.

Job opportunities change from time to time and the following brief survey of areas of employment is intended only as a guide.

RESEARCH AND DEVELOPMENT

Fundamental research into the structure and properties of materials is often termed 'pure research'. New materials arise as the result of:

- developing new polymerisation reactions;

- trying different alloying combinations for metals or ceramics;

- changing the purity level of existing materials;

- blending previously untried polymers;

- combining different materials to form composites;

- manipulating the structure of existing materials into previously unknown arrangements.

These new materials excite considerable scientific curiosity and there are, therefore, career possibilities involving the production and characterisation of new materials. Recent developments have included: lower-density aluminium–lithium alloys, to compete with polymers for aerospace applications; warm superconducting ceramics, which could revolutionise electronics; and conducting polymers, for a variety of applications where static electricity is a particular problem.

Similar possibilities exist in laboratories that attempt to improve the understanding of the properties of existing materials. Such improved understanding permits unknown behaviour to be predicted. These areas of fundamental research require access to a wide range of equipment, which is frequently highly sophisticated. This has resulted in the work being concentrated into a number of well equipped laboratories. Most of this work is funded by Government, since it takes a long time before the expenditure on fundamental research can be converted into saleable products. In recent years, the Government has been attempting to direct the money it spends on research into areas with obvious commercial potential. To focus this spending, it has established a number of interdisciplinary research centres based on universities to tackle identified problems. Several of these interdisciplinary research centres have a major input from materials science and engineering.

In Britain, there is a widespread view that applied research and development work is less intellectually demanding than fundamental research. However, the application of established knowledge to new or existing materials to achieve a defined increase in performance or decrease in cost can be very challenging. This form of 'customer-driven' research and development has been encouraged within Government-funded laboratories and has always dominated the work in industry. To be effective, good working relationships have to be developed with the works that make and use the materials under consideration. Communication skills and the ability to get on with other people are thus vitally important.

PRODUCTION MANAGEMENT

Materials-producing industries such as the steel or polymer industries need high-calibre scientists and engineers to remain competitive with overseas producers. Both cost and quality are critically important factors, which can be controlled by the application of suitable technology. These technical goals have to be reached within fixed periods of time without alienating the workforce. This combination of pressures can be very demanding, but the rewards in terms of job satisfaction and career progression are significant.

Fabrication industries have increasingly recognised the improvement in material properties that can be achieved by control of processing. This has led to the employment of a number of metallurgists in metal-working, fabrication and finishing industries. Demand has been rising for polymer technologists and ceramic engineers to make similar contributions.

MATERIALS SELECTION

Users of materials face a bewildering array of both old and new materials. In many instances, the designer faced with the problem of selecting a material falls back on well known materials. With more demanding applications, however, the materials engineer is brought into the design discussions at an early stage. Selection for some consumer items may be based largely on cost, but for other applications reliability over a long life may be more important. An understanding of the engineering problems involved is important in these circumstances, and many materials engineers progress to significant involvement in the design process itself. This close contact with finished products appeals to many people and the case study on materials for turbine blades (Section 5.4) illustrates the potential of this type of career.

TECHNICAL SALES AND MARKETING

Industrial competition is such that, unless a company actively informs its customers of its products, it is likely to go out of business. Where the products are consumer goods, very little different from those of its competitors, it is frequently the effectiveness of its sales and marketing that ensures survival. Where, however, a company's products are sold on the basis of technical performance, it is valuable to employ suitably knowledgeable salespeople to discuss the product with customers. Selling appeals to certain types of people, and personality traits are probably more important than ability as a scientist or engineer. Since the success of many companies is dependent on their sales force, they are well rewarded financially.

PROFESSIONAL DEVELOPMENT

From this survey, it is possible to see that a range of aptitudes and interests can find satisfaction in a career based on materials science or engineering. Those seeking professional recognition will have to satisfy the appropriate professional institution that their qualifications, industrial training and experience are satisfactory for membership. In the case of The Institute of Materials, those deemed eligible for membership (MIM) can also be registered as Chartered Engineers at The Engineering Council. This is a qualification recognised not only in the UK but throughout the EU, and in other countries such as the USA, Canada, Australia and New Zealand. Thus it is possible to develop a career without international limitations.

This article has been prepared by Martin Stammers, Education Officer, The Institute of Materials.

Appendix C

METALLOGRAPHY

It is interesting to see the crystals within a specimen of zinc, such as that which results from the investigation in Section 3.1. To do this, you need to be able to cut your specimen in half, and then polish it until you have achieved a clean, flat surface. Such specimen preparation is a highly skilled task, but it is possible to achieve satisfactory results if you follow the instructions below. Alternatively, you may find that a local university has a laboratory where you can prepare and observe such specimens.

For sample preparation, you will need:

- Silicon carbide grinding papers, grades P240, P400, P600, P1200

- Glass plates as a base for polishing papers

- Ethanol

- Hair drier, file, tweezers

- Zinc chemical polishing and etching solution (when made up, store in a dark bottle):

  40 g chromium(VI) oxide, CrO_3
  3 g sodium sulphate
  10 cm^3 nitric acid (concentrated)
  190 cm^3 water

1. Cut a specimen, no longer than 1 cm, from your sample. File the cut end flat and take care not to leave any sharp edges, which may tear the grinding paper. You must take care to avoid rocking the specimen during polishing. You can minimise this problem by gripping a short specimen as close to the grinding paper as possible.

2. Support the grinding papers on a hard smooth surface such as a glass plate. Wet the paper with water. Use a backwards and forwards motion to grind the specimen. Continue grinding until all scratches from the previous filing are removed.

3. Wash the specimen with water before transferring it to the next finest paper. Each time you change to a finer paper rotate the specimen through 90° and continue grinding until all the previous scratches are removed. After completing grinding on all four papers, wash the specimen thoroughly with water.

4. The specimen is now ready for chemical polishing and etching. Use a pair of stainless-steel tweezers to hold the specimen. Immerse it in the polishing and etching solution and agitate it gently for a few seconds. Remove it from the solution and rinse it under cold running water.

5. Inspect the polished surface for grain structure. Repeat the immersion and rinsing sequence until the grain structure is clearly seen.

6. Wash the specimen in ethanol and dry it using hot air. Make a sketch of the grain structure that you observe. You should obtain results similar to those shown in Figs 3.6(a) and (b).

Hazard warning
Wear goggles and protective gloves.

Appendix D

RESOURCES

USEFUL ADDRESSES

The Institute of Materials, 1 Carlton House Terrace, London SW1Y 5DB
(Leaflets on all materials; loan of videos; speakers; careers information;
contact the Education Officer)

The Institute of Physics, 47 Belgrave Square, London SW1X 8QX
(Careers information, schools, publications, speakers, etc.)

Centre for Studies in Science and Mathematics Education, School of
Education, The University of Leeds, Leeds LS2 9JT
(Publications; courses for teachers)

CONTACTING YOUR LOCAL UNIVERSITY

A local university or college may well be prepared to show you round, to
share their laboratory facilities with you, or to provide speakers. The
Institute of Materials provides an introduction service, to help you make
the appropriate contacts. Write to the Education Officer at the above
address.

APPARATUS AND MATERIALS

Most of the experimental work involves apparatus and materials that are
readily available from commercial suppliers.

- Polaroid (with integral quarter-wave plate) and Photoflex sheet for
  photoelastic stress analysis may be obtained from:
  Sharples Stress Engineers Ltd, Unit 331, Walton Summit Centre,
  Bamber Bridge, Preston, Lancs PR5 8AR

- Grinding and polishing materials for metallographic specimens may be
  obtained from:
  Beuhler UK Ltd, Science Park, University of Warwick, Coventry CV4
  7EZ

BOOKS AND OTHER SOURCES

Books

The Architecture of Solids, G. E. Bacon, 1981, Taylor and Francis.
Telecommunications in Practice, British Telecom, 1985, BT/ASE.
The New Science of Strong Materials, J. E. Gordon, 1976, Pelican.
The Structure of Matter, André Guinier, 1984, Arnold.
Elementary Science of Metals, J. W. Martin, 1974, Taylor and Francis.
Introduction to Polymer Science, L. R. G. Treloar, 1982, Taylor and Francis.
Metals in the Service of Man, William Alexander and Arthur Street, 1985,
Pelican.
The Cambridge Guide to the Material World, Rodney Cotterill, 1985,
Cambridge University Press.

Structures, J. E. Gordon, 1978, Pelican.
The Structure and Properties of Solids, Bruce Chalmers, 1982, Heyden.
Tomorrow's Materials, Ken Easterling, 1988, Institute of Materials.
Materials, Principles and Practice, C. Newey and G. Weaver, 1990, Open
    University.
Science of Structures and Materials, J. E. Gordon, *Scientific American* Library,
    1988, W. H. Freeman.
'Materials for Economic Growth', *Scientific American*, October 1986.

Other sources

SATIS 16–19
Several units produced by the SATIS (Science and Technology in Society)
16–19 Project relate to aspects of materials science. These provide some
useful activities that could be used in parallel with this book. Published by
the Association for Science Education.

- Unit 23: Stick or slip?

- Unit 47: Playing safe

- Unit 71: Plug into safety

- Unit 72: Cracking up

- Unit 98: Optical fibres

- Unit 99: Making a racket

- Unit 100: The physics of racket games

GNVQ Science
GNVQ Science (Level 3) has a strong emphasis on the physics and
    chemistry of materials. Related publications include:

GNVQ Advanced Science, Ken Gadd and John Holman, 1995, Thomas
    Nelson.
GNVQ Science: Advanced, Nuffield Science in Practice, 1995, Heinemann.

Index